THE Inventor's Master Plan

A compact guide through the six essential phases of the inventing process.

Published by United Inventors Association
in conjunction with *Inventors' Digest* Magazine

THE Inventor's Master Plan

Publisher's Cataloging in Publication

Provided by Quality Books, Inc.

The inventor's master plan: a compact guide through the six essential phases of the inventing process. - - 1st ed.
p. cm.
"Published by United Inventors Association in conjunction with Inventors' Digest magazine."

1. Inventions--United States. I United Inventors Association of the USA. II. Title: Inventors' Digest (Boston, Mass.)

T212.I58 2001 608
QB101-200908

ISBN: 0-9712367-2-0

About the United Inventors Association:

The UIA is a not-for-profit, 501-C-3 corporation. Its mission is to provide leadership, support, and services to inventor support groups, as well as to other organizations and individuals interested in continuing America's role as the world's leader in innovation and invention. The UIA is affiliated with the Academy of Applied Science. The UIA is co-founder of National Inventors' Month - August.

Sponsors:

Academy of Applied Science, 24 Warren Street, Concord, NH 03301 (www.aas-world.org)

Other publications of the United Inventors Association:

THE Inventor's Resource Guide, a brief manual that provides an introduction to the key points of guidance to the inventor.

THE Inventor's Journal, a record keeping journal.

Affiliate publications:

Inventors' Digest, the only inventor magazine published in the United States. Subscribe through us by ordering from our web site; by credit card via telephone; or by check or money order mailed to the address below.

The United Inventors Association
P. O. Box 23447 • Rochester, New York 14692
phone 716-359-9310 • fax 716-359-1132
web site: www.uiausa.org • e-mail: uiausa@aol.com

Contents

Page

About the authors . . .

Jeffrey Dobkin is the author of *How to Market a Product for Under $500,* and *Uncommon Marketing Techniques.* He is a board member of United Inventors Association and American Society for Inventors, both not-for-profit and is a prominent writer and speaker on publicizing and marketing inventions.

Joanne Hayes-Rines is the editor and publisher of *Inventors' Digest,* www.inventorsdigest.com, the only North American magazine solely for inventors. She has served as Vice President and President of United Inventors Association, is an activist for inventors' rights and is a prominent speaker at inventor workshops across the country.

Donald Grant Kelly is Chief Executive Officer of The Academy of Applied Science, a non-profit educational institution. He spent more than 35 years in the intellectual property arena, most of that with the U.S. Patent and Trademark Office. He served as Patent Examiner, Examining Group Director and Executive Assistant to the Commissioner. As a member of the USPTO Commissioner's senior executive staff, Kelly established and directed the Office of Independent Inventor Programs. He is a prominent and frequent speaker at inventor conferences, expositions and workshops.

Jack Lander has served as President of United Inventors Association, Vice President of Yankee Invention Exposition, founder of Innovators Guild (all not-for-profit), is a book author, and regular columnist for *Inventors' Digest.* Jack, a prolific inventor with several patents, teaches courses in successful inventing. He is also a speaker at inventor workshops and is the editor and a contributor to this book.

Lisa Lloyd is a board member of United Inventors Association. She is an accomplished inventor who has patented and licensed five of her her own inventions and is the founder of Invention University.

Robert Mason, Esq. is a registered patent attorney and a board member of United Inventors Association. He is the co-creator of Patent Pro, a popular and highly regarded computerized system for preparing patent applications.

Gerald Udell, Ph.D., is the creator of the long-respected PIES (Preliminary Invention Evaluation System), the premier evaluation system in the U. S. He is a board member of United Inventors Association, a professor of marketing at Southwest Missouri State University and has been published in a variety of academic and professional journals.

* * *

And many thanks to jini Lander for her eagle eye in reading every word, and spotting typos, inconsistencies and expressions that were abstruse.

Introduction

Inventing can be a risky business. Commonly quoted statistics will tell you that successful inventions are somewhere in the 2 to 5 percent range. And "success" is modestly defined as any invention that earns more than its cost of patenting, prototyping, and getting it to market - - in other words, the total cost you incur from concept until you realize income.

Don't despair. A more recent study by Ron Westrum, Ph.D., and Ed Zimmer revealed that 13 percent of first-time inventors were successful in licensing their inventions, and those who chose to manage the production and marketing of their inventions attained a success level of 49 percent.

Even these odds can be discouraging if your goal is to license. But consider this: Most of the inventors who didn't succeed were inventors who *did not make the effort to study the processes by which inventors become successful.* The fact that you are now reading these words shows that you understand that there is more to inventing than merely coming up with a great idea, and writing a few letters to corporations that will welcome you with checkbook in hand. (In fact, when inventors don't succeed, the main reasons are that they don't seek information, they lack a plan, they fail to manage, and they don't persist, rather than because their invention lacks merit.) The point here is that you recognize the importance of studying the methods used by successful inventors, and you adopt those methods.

The master plan we present here consists of six main steps plus an appendix that covers financing. We placed financing last, and optional, because until you create a budget based on the six critical steps, you probably won't have a sound idea of how much money you will need, or what your options are for its sources in the case where you cannot finance your plan yourself.

You will notice that the first critical step in the master plan is *not to file a patent application.* The patent application is step five for a good reason: You many not need or want a patent after you have worked through the first four steps. And until you have a prototype, your attorney or agent may not have a complete picture of the features around which sound claims can be written. So, the sequence in which the steps are accomplished is important to getting the most from the plan.

Finally, this book is purposely brief and concentrated because we want you to read it all before you invest any money. There are many good books available that offer considerable depth in most of the six steps, especially prior art searching, patenting, and marketing. We encourage you to read these books to polish the knowledge we present here. For example, *Patent It Yourself*, by David Pressman, Esq., is an excellent source of information that can save you thousands of dollars in obtaining your patent whether you decide to write your own application (which we don't encourage) or have it prepared by a patent attorney or patent agent. These books are available through the UIA when you are ready.

Now: Read. Plan. Manage. Persist.

Good luck; but, then, luck is the least of it.

* * *

The Power of 2^2
(You're not alone!)

by Joanne Hayes-Rines

Publisher, Inventors' Digest
Vice President, United Inventors Association

When a person gets an idea for a new product and discovers that he has the "fire in the belly" that it takes to want to bring that product to market, he often finds himself in an awkward position. He wants to learn how to develop the idea but is afraid to talk to anyone about it. He doesn't know whom to trust or where to turn.

The first step to overcome fear is education and that is the reason the officers of the United Inventors Association have banded together to create this book. We wanted to provide novice inventors with the "ammunition" they need to begin the process of new product development.

Even with the detailed, real world information included in this book, readers will quickly realize as they move forward with their new product concept that they are encountering challenges unique to their situation. They have questions that are not specifically answered in this book. Where should they turn? What should they do to get the answers they need? To whom should they talk?

They should turn to others who have "been there, done that," as they say. They should turn to other inventors who have trod the same path, made their own mistakes and learned some of the pitfalls and many of the positive ways to develop a concept.

Where do you find such veterans of the invention development battles? Across the country there are thousands of people who belong to inventors' organizations, and they provide unique, powerful networking opportunities that all who are serious about their ideas should take advantage of.

When the United Inventors Association was created in 1990, most inventor organizations had little, if any, connection with each other. They operated alone and most knew little about the other organizations if they even knew they existed. There was no formal list of inventor organizations - - no contact information - - no easy way to find out about the other groups - - no easy way for individuals to discover the existence of a group in their area.

Today it's a different story. Leaders of inventors' organizations are united through the UIA newsletter and through direct contact with each other and the UIA headquarters. Contact information for groups (phone numbers, addresses, e-mail addresses) are kept current by the UIA, and this information is available at www.uiausa.org.

The wise and serious inventor should take advantage of the services offered by inventors' groups. Most groups hold monthly meetings and feature a guest speaker who shares knowledge about specific product development steps, such as prototyping, marketing, evaluations, etc. After their formal presentation, these speakers usually answer specific questions from the audience so the attendees have the opportunity to have their own unique problems addressed.

Several groups around the country conduct special invention evaluation meetings. The attendees are group members who comment on each other's inventions. The experienced members offer suggestions about prototyping, marketing, design and other aspects of the potential product that the inventor may not have considered. Confidentiality agreements are signed before the disclosures are made.

Members of inventor organizations include service providers, such as prototype makers, patent attorneys and agents, who are respected by the organization. These professionals often offer free advice and consultation to group members as well as providing fee-based services.

Beyond a doubt, the most important reason why inventors should join an inventors' group is for the networking that is available. When faced with the problem of how to get a prototype made, the answer can be found by talking with other group members. When considering a marketing firm, the easiest way to find out if it is a reputable firm is to ask other group members. Want to know when there are conferences, trade shows or other events in your local area that might help you develop your invention? Join a local inventors group and receive their newsletter.

Becoming an active, involved, contributing member of an inventors' group will keep you focused on your product. You won't avoid all of the possible mistakes that you could make but you'll certainly minimize them. You'll get the encouragement and support you need when it seems as if you've gone down a dead end.

There are approximately 125 inventors groups around the country which is, obviously, not enough to serve all those who are in need. If you are one of the unlucky inventors without a group in your area, there are two things you can do. You could join the nearest group and at least get put on their mailing list to receive the newsletter and any other information they supply to their members. While you may not be able to attend meetings, you will have a network of people whom you can contact when you have specific questions. In no time you'll find that the annual dues (which are usually very modest) will be one of the best expenditures you could make.

If you want to be actively involved in a group, take advantage of the UIA's program to help inventors start groups in areas where none exist. Contact the UIA headquarters and they will guide you through the process of networking with others to start your own group.

By networking with other inventors -- many of whom have products on the market -- you'll maximize your chances for success on your good ideas and learn when to put aside those ideas that may not be worth developing. It's your choice: you can take the invention development journey all alone or you can speed up the process by networking with others.

When you look at it that way, the right choice seems obvious, doesn't it?

* * *

Phase 1: Defining Your Invention

by Jack Lander

"If you can't write it, you don't know it." That may sound a bit radical, but it's what one of my professors told me years ago.

To some extent this admonition applies to inventors. Until we define our invention in exhaustive written detail, including at least rough sketches, if not drawings, we may not really know it. We know it as "an idea for an invention," of course; but we may not have resolved our idea into "hardware" - - the essential details, features, and components that work together to produce the effect we seek. (Not all inventions involve hardware, of course; but it illustrates the point.)

You may not define your invention completely until you make your prototype, test it, and refine it. But you should carefully explain your invention on paper as soon as you have a clear initial concept of its function and features. This written definition serves four main purposes:

1. it establishes your initial journal entry, and the date of conception against which all future changes will be recorded and dated.

2. it explains your invention to an evaluator.

3. it explains your invention to the person who will search prior art (mainly patents).

4. it serves as the basis for preparing your patent application, both the writing and the drawing.

Conception date and logging. In the United States, the first person to invent is usually considered to be the rightful inventor. But this rule does not entitle an inventor to dream up an invention, make a dated journal entry, and indefinitely postpone further development. In effect, such inventor could eliminate other inventors from the race by having documented evidence of being the first to invent, invalidating a recent inventor's patent, and claiming patent rights for himself. An inventor must not only establish a date of conception, but must diligently pursue the development of his or her invention. And to prove that you are developing your inventions, you should keep a journal. Make frequent entries, let's say at least once a week. Don't leave any gaps. Make entries in ink. Have key entries witnessed by one or two others who are not a relative, your spouse, or anyone who may eventually share in any profits from your invention. *THE Inventor's Journal,* available from UIA, is an excellent choice, although any blank book with sewn or glued binding and sequentially numbered pages will do.

Professional evaluating. One of the most valuable steps an inventor can take is that of obtaining a professional evaluation of his or her invention. (Covered in the next chapter.) The evaluators need a detailed definition of your invention, preferably including sketches, in order to do the best job.

Prior art searching. In most cases we inventors order a basic patent search which does not include a search of foreign patents, and trade journals and magazines. In the case of a "high tech" invention, or one that has exceptional potential for profit, an "extended search" can be made. Such a search is much more expensive than the usual patent search. In either case, the searcher needs a detailed definition of the invention and its purpose.

Writing the patent application. By the time you are ready to apply for your patent you may have made several changes to your invention. These changes, recorded in your journal, and added to your original definition of your invention, along with your prototype, if available, become essential background from which your patent attorney or agent fully understands your invention. A clear statement of the purpose of your invention, how it serves that purpose, and the details of its features and components may make the diference between a strong or a weak patent.

Format. There is no standard format for writing the definition of your invention. However, it makes sense to title it "Confidential Disclosure," because you are disclosing your invention in detail, and you should make known to every reader that this document is confidential, and its content is not to be disclosed to anyone else without your consent.

University affiliated evaluators, patent searchers, and patent attorneys and agents need to know the problem, annoyance, need, or want that you believe your invention will solve. For example, if an inventor orders a search on aspirin as a supplement for increasing the rate at which hogs gain weight, this is a new use for the aspirin, and may be patentable even though its patent as a pain reliever ran out years ago. Seldom will an invention serve such a radically different purpose. But the point is to be very specific.

Since "purpose" gets back to "problem, annoyance, need, or want," start your Confidential Disclosure with the most appropriate of these words. Use one or more of these key words in the body of your writing as well as in the caption.

Next, it is helpful to state how the problem (etc.) presently is solved or accommodated. Your readers will be helped by knowing what has been done in the past that you now propose to improve. In many cases the new invention is not at all similar to the former solution.

Now, describe how your invention solves or accommodates the problem, annoyance, need, or want. Caption this section something like: "How my invention solves this problem."

Finally, describe the details of the features of your invention, and how these features assemble and work together. This section should be accompanied by numbered sketches that illustrate your words.

Example:

CONFIDENTIAL DISCLOSURE

The annoyance and need.

Today's desktop appliances result in an insufficiency of electrical outlets below the desk. We have computers, printers, scanners, modems, fax machines, answering machines, cell phone battery chargers, cordless phone power supplies and desk lamps all competing for outlets. Some of these devices use the small, cube-shaped power supplies that hog space on outlet strips, usually occupying the space of three outlets due to their size and configuration.

Existing solution.

The required number of outlets are obtained the hard way, by adding another power strip or two. Such arrangement is unsightly, cumbersome, space-consuming and very difficult to clean.

How my invention solves this annoyance and need.

My invention, which I call "The Outrigger," is a dual outlet into which one or two of the cube-shaped power supplies plug. The Outrigger is, in turn, plugged into the main power strip, but occupies only one outlet space. The net effect is a neat arrangement that typically frees up five outlets on the strip, thereby eliminating the need for a second or even third power strip and the mess.

Features and details of The Outrigger.

The Outrigger, in effect, is a hard-packaged extension cord. (See sketches on pages 2 and 3.) Its novel and hopefully main patentable feature is the plug, which can be rotated 90 degrees to accommodate the two different outlet orientations on various power strips. See sketch 1. Rotation of the plug presents the problem of how to conduct current to the outlets. This can be done with either a commutator or flexible wire. Flex wire is the most simple and least expensive solution, but has the disadvantage of the eventual fatigue and fraying or breaking of the wire. But once The Outrigger is in place, chances are that no plug rotation will ever again be made. For this reason, and for economy, I have chosen the flex wire solution rather than the more complex, expensive and potentially troublesome commutator.

This Confidential Disclosure consists of three sheets, of which sheets two and three are sketches. I declare that I am the sole inventor of The Outrigger.

______________________________(signed) ______________(dated)

The example above is brief. Yours should be more explicit in its features and details section.

Phase 2:

Evaluating Your Invention's Commercial Potential

by Gerald G. Udell, Ph.D.

Just what is the big deal about invention evaluation? I know my idea will sell and, besides, all my friends and family tell me it will be a big winner.

Take a hint from the pros. The concept of idea/invention evaluation has been around for quite some time and is widely practiced in industry. About 90 percent of major product marketing firms use some form of formal evaluation to screen their new product ideas and inventions. The reason is simple: Most ideas and inventions lack commercial feasibility.

The idea mortality rate varies, depending upon the industry involved; studies suggest that it takes from 40 to 350 ideas to generate one new product. Now add to this a new product failure rate of between 34 percent and 90 percent for established businesses and the odds are not very good, even for companies that are skilled in the art of marketing new products. The best-case scenario is that it takes about 136 ideas to generate one successful new product in the corporate world. The worst-case scenario is that only about one in 3,150 will reach the winner's circle. These companies know that the best and most economical way to improve these odds is to weed out those ideas of low potential and high risk.

So does this apply to independent inventors? Aren't inventors better at inventing than corporations? There is data that indicates that smaller entities are more creative than big organizations, but getting beyond the idea stage frequently requires resources and skills not readily available to the average inventor. Bringing a new product to market can be a costly, complicated and time-consuming affair.

The odds you face are higher than those faced by established enterprises because you face additional barriers and risk factors. Starting a new venture to launch a new product is typically very risky, especially if you do not have solid business experience in product marketing. Likewise, licensing is difficult at best as many, if not most, corporations have strong negative attitudes toward outside new-product ideas and independent inventors. There isn't any solid research on the inventor's idea mortality rate, but estimates range from 99 in 100 to over 999 in 1,000. In other words, the chances of reaching the marketplace are between 1 in 100 and 1 in 1,000 and some would argue that they are a good deal higher. In contrast, the odds of winning on a single try at a slot machine in Missouri are about 1 in 7.

So, why evaluate? Evaluation may be necessary for others, you say, but it does not apply to me. I know my invention will sell. Besides, *I* evaluated my idea, and I even asked some friends and relatives about it.

Whoa, there is a problem here. Unless you are a very unusual inventor, or have been down this road many times before, you probably do not have the background or objectivity necessary to evaluate your own ideas and inventions. On several occasions I have experimented with self-evaluation techniques. The experiments weren't a failure, but the techniques were. What the research revealed was that self-evaluation frequently creates a false sense of optimism, leaving the inventor worse off than he or she was before.

As for friends and family, the chances are you told them all about your invention. The odds are that they aren't about to tell you anything negative. Let's face it, when was the last time you told a friend or relative that their new baby was really ugly? Brainchildren (inventions) get the same diplomatic treatment.

Now, if you like your invention, you aren't alone; most of us like our own ideas, particularly if we have committed time, attention, effort and money to them. Corporate inventors get excited about and committed to their ideas just like you. This is why in the corporate world evaluation is usually assigned to someone not directly involved in the project and who is skilled in the art. That is also why you are probably not a good candidate to evaluate your own ideas or inventions. And this is the primary reason for the UIA/PIES Evaluation Service. We want to encourage innovation and get you off on the right track.

The UIA/PIES Evaluation Service

Corporate evaluation systems typically highlight those factors considered to be important to success within that company. We built our evaluation format around many of the same factors, plus those important to independent inventors. We have grouped our evaluation criteria into like groupings:

PIES-X Evaluation Criteria

<u>Societal Criteria</u>
- Legality
- Safety
- Environmental Impact
- Societal Impact

<u>Business Risk Criteria</u>
- Functional Feasibility
- Production
- Stage of Development
- Investment Costs
- Payback Period
- Profitability
- Marketing Research
- Research and Development

Demand Analysis Criteria
- Potential Market
- Potential Sales
- Trend of Demand
- Stability of Demand
- Product Life Cycle
- Product Line Potential

Market Acceptance Criteria
- Compatibility
- Learning
- Need
- Dependence
- Visibility
- Promotion
- Distribution
- Service

Competitive Criteria
- Appearance
- Function
- Durability
- Price
- Existing Competition
- New Competition
- Protection

Experience and Strategy Criteria
- Technology Transfer
- New Venture
- Marketing Experience
- Technical Experience
- Financial Experience
- Management/Production Experience
- Initial Distribution Strategy
- Market Entry Barriers
- Overall Market Attractiveness

At the conclusion of the evaluation we ask our evaluators to summarize their evaluation in one final overall assessment of the commercial potential of, and the risks associated with, the project under review. This summary judgment then drives our final recommendation. If we feel that the risks are too high, or the potential payoff is too low, we'll say so. We realize that getting a negative review is not a pleasant experience, but there is something far more unpleasant - facing family, friends, and self after making an investment of time, money and effort to pursue a dream only to have it and our investment evaporate.

We try to avoid the question, "Is this a good idea?" There are a few really poor ideas that do quite well in the marketplace, at least in the short run and there are a lot of really good ideas that never make it to first base. The central issue is the ability of your idea or invention to provide you with a return that is sufficient to reward you for your investment and to compensate you for the risks that you have taken.

There are always barriers in your path and risks to be considered. Some inventions might look like they will pay off, but what about the risks involved? Your invention will need to yield sufficient returns to yield a profit and compensate you for the risks that you have taken. For example, some potentially viable inventions are very difficult to license and many new products are incredibly difficult to launch from a small business platform. Reaching the marketplace is never easy, not even for those with experience and resources to burn.

Our evaluation format is designed to alert you to some of the barriers you will likely face and it may suggest some alternatives to you. A lot of inventors/entrepreneurs fail because they become enamored with the high volume sales of national chain discount stores when they should be focusing their initial efforts on channels of distribution that are more suitable to their invention/product. We address this issue in the PIES-X format. However, its primary function is to help you make more informed decisions about the wisdom of investing more time, energy and resources in your project; and this is only part of our objective.

It is also our hope to provide you with deeper insights into the innovation process and better equip you for the challenges that lie ahead. That is why every inventor participating in the UIA/PIES Evaluation Service receives a copy of our evaluation manual, as well as a copy of this book. We are committed to education as being the best way to help inventors realize their dreams and to stimulate the flow of innovations into the marketplace, making this a better place for all of us to live.

Background of the UIA/PIES Evaluation Service
The PIES format is based on a very simple concept that I discovered as a brand new MBA working for General Electric in 1967. We had invested a lot of time and effort along with about $750,000 on a new product that failed miserably in marketplace. Since I had been involved in the project I figured that there were a few things my professors had forgotten to tell me about. So, I sat down and began to list the factors that contributed to the failure of the GE Letterwriter. When I finished I reached a startling conclusion - - most of the reasons on that list should have been obvious to us before we even started the project. In short, some very good people working for a very good company, well known for its ability to innovate, had blown it (big time). I asked why. This question led to startling conclusion #2. We didn't get the answers because we didn't ask the questions. My research since then indicates that *the failure to properly screen potential new products is the most common reason for failure.*

I did not know it at the time, but this product failure was the genesis of what has become known as the PIES (Preliminary Innovation Evaluation System) now used by the United Inventors Association to evaluate inventions and new product ideas. PIES-I was the result of an effort to develop a formal, systematic and comprehensive evaluation format designed specifically to meet the evaluation needs of independent and small business inventors.

Launched in 1974 as part of a National Science Foundation innovation center experiment at the University of Oregon, the PIES format has been under continuous improvement at the Innovation Institute since the conclusion of that experiment in 1979. It is estimated that over 30,000 new product ideas have been evaluated using the several versions of the PIES format and modifications thereof. *Editor's note: Innovation Institute is now a branch of Southwest Missouri State University.*

PIES is perhaps the best known and most widely used formal evaluation format in the world designed specifically to meet the needs of independent inventors. For over ten years PIES was used by the Wal-Mart Innovation Network to evaluate inventions and new products in cooperation with Wal-Mart Stores, Inc. The Wal-Mart program still exists, although the Wal-Mart name was dropped in an effort to reduce inventor confusion. Too many inventors thought that the evaluations were done by Wal-Mart or that a positive report was a guarantee of an order from the retailer. The UIA evaluation service uses PIES-X, the tenth and most recent revision of the original PIES format.

The Primary Purpose of the UIA/PIES Evaluation Service

Innovation evaluation is the easiest and least costly part of the process that lies ahead. This doesn't mean that it is a stage to be skipped. Mistakes become increasingly costly as you progress further into the innovation process. Expect to invest a good deal of time, money and effort in your project, even if you want to sell it to someone else. Getting to the point where others will be interested can be fairly costly.

Corporate evaluations

Even in the corporate world, innovation is a very risky affair. Corporations use evaluation to help them manage the risks inherent in the innovation process by weeding out high-risk projects as early as possible, and then devoting their efforts to those with the highest expected pay off. This is the same reason inventors should seek the assistance of a recognized professional evaluation service. Simply put, systematic evaluation is the easiest and least costly way to improve your prospects for success. However, risk management is not the only purpose of evaluation.

Improving Invention (and Inventor) Credibility

A positive evaluation by a recognized professional third

party generally will help improve your credibility with potential investors or licensees. Getting past the "Not Invented Here" attitude and the negative impression of inventors held by most corporations is very difficult. While a positive professional evaluation won't compensate for a poor presentation of an idea, it will help improve the overall impression and it will help open doors. It may be the factor that causes someone to take a second look at your invention or to help you get past the clerical screen.

Corporations and sophisticated investors are accustomed and impervious to claims of great commercial potential. In fact, such claims make them nervous. When inventors expect too much from their inventions, they will typically expect too much of the corporate licensee. What the corporations don't expect, and seldom get, is an inventor who takes the time to obtain a qualified third-party opinion. From the corporate perspective, such evaluation speaks well of the inventor.

Assisting in Decision Making

There is a fundamental difference between evaluation in the corporate world and the inventor world. In the corporate world evaluation is a decision-making tool. That is, the evaluator frequently makes the decision. This is never the case in the inventor world. Here, evaluation is a tool to aid the inventor in making decisions. While an inventor may rely heavily upon such input, it is he or she who must make the decision as to what to do next. The purpose of the evaluation is to help the inventor to make a better, more informed decision. People vary greatly in terms of their circumstances, resources and willingness to take risks. These factors must also be factored into the decision-making process.

Even if the final recommendation is very positive, it is not time to throw caution to the wind. Even under the very best of circumstances innovation is a risky affair. Those who plow ahead without thought or careful planning generally bear the consequences. Careful attention to details is always in order. Taking the time to become informed and to get the help you need is the least risky approach to reaching the marketplace.

If, on the other hand, your final evaluation score is not very good, automatic abandonment of your project may not be the best alternative. Carefully thought out and well reasoned decisions are always appropriate. Weigh the potential risks and rewards carefully and then make your decision. Study your evaluation report and the evaluation manual carefully. It may well be that there are some things you can do to lower your risks or improve your returns, but don't assume that improving your mousetrap will automatically improve your chances of success. The issues at hand may have little to do with the mechanics or design of your invention. The devil is often in the details of the marketplace. For example, improving the performance or lowering the cost of a new buggy whip isn't likely to bring about much change in the demand for buggy whips. Similarly, improving design is not likely to increase your prospects of licensing if corporate minds are already closed. Make sure your responses have a chance of succeeding before you devote more time, money and effort to your project.

Increasing Insight Into the Nature of the Innovation Process

Any evaluation process worth its weight in salt, or sand for that matter, ought to help an inventor improve his or her understanding of the innovation process. That is why UIA has incorporated evaluation into its educational program. Since its inception, the PIES format has always had a strong educational component. This is why each PIES report has always been accompanied with an evaluation manual detailing and explaining the PIES evaluation process.

The first PIES evaluation manual was published in 1974 to assist inventors in understanding the variables involved in the evaluation process and to explain how they interrelate to impact on the commercial potential of an invention. Each evaluation criteria in the report is keyed by page number to a discussion of that criterion in the PIES Evaluation Manual. For example, it does little good for us to advise someone that there is a violation of existing use patterns present in their invention if they do not understand this concept or how it can have a very major impact on the potential of an invention. As you read this book and acquire a broader perspective of invention commercialization, you will better understand the PIES format and its accompanying report.

Before you make any decisions affecting the further development of your invention, we suggest that you read the PIES-X Evaluation Manual that will be sent to you as soon as your evaluation request is received. This will help you understand the PIES-X format and your report. We will have attempted to ask and answer the right questions. It may also be helpful to you to review the rest of the materials we have supplied.

The UIA Resource Network

If your project has received at least marginal overall final assessment, we will send you a list of potential resources located in your area. Some of these resources may be helpful to you in deciding your next step. We have included a variety of resources including Small Business Development Centers, professional licensing agents (who work only on a commission basis and do not charge other fees), economic development groups, prototype makers and the like. Not all states are uniform in the availability of inventor resources. Consequently, while our resources are quite good in some states, they are modest in others. In addition, there is a lot of turnover, especially in taxpayer funded programs. Updating this directory is very expensive. Therefore, we can do so about every two years. Expect some resources to have changed their policies or to have ceased operations. Stay up to date by visiting our web site at www.uiausa.org

Why the UIA/PIES Evaluation Service

There are others who claim to evaluate your inventions or will offer to research your invention. So, why should you use the UIA/PIES service? First, our service is based on the most up-to-date version of the PIES format. No evaluation system tailor made to serve the needs of independent inventors has more research poured into it over an extended period of time than the PIES format.

Even more importantly, evaluation and education are the only services we provide. This is your assurance of our objectivity. We are not in this business to provide you with other services. We won't follow up on a positive evaluation report with another round of fee-based services. This assures you of our objectivity. Expect us to tell you what our analysis has revealed. Expect the truth as we see it. We are here to help you make better decisions about your inventions.

* * *

Editor's note: If you have not yet requested evaluation of your invention through the United Inventors Association, you may obtain an application by contacting the UIA office or visiting our web site.

United Inventors Association

P. O. Box 23447

Rochester, New York 14692

Phone 716-359-9310 • Fax 716-359-1132

Web site: www.uiausa.org

e-mail: UIAUSA@aol.com

Editor's notes continued:

The UIA-PIES evaluation process carries a pledge of confidentiality, and is therefore the safest means of evaluation before your regular patent application is filed. After your patent issues, you may cautiously consider supplemental sources of evaluation. Here are three important channels for such evaluation:

- *Buyers in chain stores,*
- *Catalog buyers, and*
- *Selling in local stores.*

Buyers in giant chains, such as The Home Depot, Office Max, Wal-Mart, etc., are generally reluctant to take on products that have not proved themselves through sales in smaller chains or independent stores. Buyers must be alert to new products to replace those that are no longer selling well. And a good buyer will have a sixth sense about which products will succeed in his or her stores. A personal meeting with the appropriate chain buyer may be enlightening. Present your product as not yet ready for the larger chain; you are merely asking the buyer's opinion based on his or her experience. Stress that your product is patented. Some chains have been known to "borrow" a good product idea, and engage their favorite sources for its manufacture.

If your invention is ready for sale in quantity, and appropriate for catalog selling, catalog buyers will provide no-nonsense evaluations. They'll either negotiate an initial order, or they'll decline. If they decline, ask what might be done to make your product 'catalog viable.' Price too high? Too difficult to explain in a short paragraph? Wrong catalog (customer profile doesn't match your product)? Too much of a niche item for a general audience, etc.? Unlike contacts with chain buyers, catalog negotiations may be carried out via mail, fax, etc. The 15,000 plus catalogers in the U.S. can be located through the Catalog of Catalogs, most likely in your library system. Catalogers are typically inventor-friendly. They depend on novelty.

Sales at the local level may be a revealing test. But be sure that you are not asking for any special treatment, such as a prominent display. If your product sells well and profitably without any favoritism, you know that you have a winner. Consider the words of Sophocles nearly 2500 years ago:

> *"Knowledge must come through action; you can have no test which is not fanciful save by trial."*

* * *

Phase 3: Patent Searching: The Art of Finding the Prior Art

by Donald Grant Kelly

CEO, The Academy of Applied Science

Creators of inventions, under United States patent laws, are entitled to patent grants. As with all entitlements, however, there are conditions. Patents pass only to inventors with new or novel inventions. And it's important to know that, even if an invention is new - - in fact, never before seen anywhere on the face of the planet - - it won't qualify for a patent if a patent examiner judges the invention to be no more than an obvious variation of known technology.

Is your invention new? Is it more than an obvious variation? How is one to know?

These questions are answered at least a thousand times each day at the US Patent and Trademark Office (USPTO) as patent examiners go about the challenging task of reviewing inventions for patentability determinations. It can take years to gain the legal expertise necessary for making such judgments, especially in light of relevant, previous publications known as "prior art." But, making those key decisions is barely half the examiner's job.

The "art of finding the prior art" can be just as daunting, and may take even the most adept searchers many hours or even days of intensive digging. To paraphrase a famous quote, the crucial question is this: "What did the public know and when did they know it?" And the job of searching is becoming more difficult every day, as technology expands at heart-stopping rates.

If all this poses problems for seasoned pros, it should go without saying that the novice inventor striving to cope with the concept of patent searching will be overwhelmed. Nonetheless, this is a task inventors should face up to prior to making serious financial commitments. Patent searching, however, isn't something that an inventor can simply run out and do. Nor is it a task to be commissioned to professionals without first gaining some basic understanding as to what is being purchased and why it may be necessary. It is for this reason that guidance on patent searching has been included as a feature of this publication.

* * *

This chapter is intended to reduce the mystery and misery of the patent search. It will outline a number of reasons for performing a patent search, and explain why the earliest possible review of relevant information can be key to success. We'll explore optional approaches to the searching task, and show where search files can be found, in both paper and electronic media. You'll read about the more common tools and resources available to assist struggling inventors in locating and accessing prior art. Finally, you'll find advice on where and when to turn for professional help in searching and the importance of advance advisory opinions on the prospect of patentability.

Why am I doing this

Undoubtedly, once you are deep into the search effort and you are confronted with hundreds if not thousands of patents and other forms of technical descriptions, the haunting question will arise time and again: "Why, exactly, am I doing this?"

A successful inventor will usually admit to the value of what is commonly referred to as the "pre-x" search of the technical literature. Many say this step is the most beneficial of all investments in the patent procurement process. The term pre-x is shorthand for "pre-examination," meaning that the search is carried out before the patentability question comes before the patent examiner. The value of the pre-x search is greatly enhanced if it is accompanied by a preliminary patentability opinion expressed by a skilled practitioner. More on this later.

Few searchers beyond the walls of the USPTO can match the acumen of the typical patent examiner in reviewing huge quantities of literature, including the patent files and other technological disclosures. Not only do they know the best techniques and sources for searching; they also are usually highly experienced in narrowly defined technical fields.

A patent examiner schooled in mechanical engineering, for example, may spend a professional lifetime as an expert in the "art" of internal combustion engines or conveyors. Others may spend their waking hours working and studying details of hydraulic valves or exercise equipment. In other words, examiners get to know their fields like no one else, and they know very well where to find the most minute details.

As a budding patent searcher, you're unlikely to ever play in their league, but you can learn enough about the process to make intelligent decisions about your own invention. Even a minimal pre-x (pre-examination) search can place you well ahead of the game. Here's why.

The State of the Art

By unearthing relevant prior art before the task falls to the hands of a patent examiner, the inventor can gain valuable insight for assessing the likelihood of success. Knowing more about the "state of the art" can aid crucial decisions about the required scope of claims to be submitted, and, perhaps more importantly, about the advisability of filing.

The outcome, in any case, is that the odds of receiving a favorable decision from the examiner can be significantly improved through a diligent preliminary patent search. Besides, there is always the possibility that an early search will reveal that the invention already exists - - and this might be considered both bad and good news for the inventor. While the discovery of patent-blocking prior art can be deflating, discovering it in time will avoid wasting thousands of dollars on legal and administrative expenses in filing an application destined to be rejected.

Apart from avoiding wasted funds, there are other important reasons for performing patent searches, and for embarking on those searches early in the innovation process.

A thorough patent search can reveal the handiwork of others who have invented solutions to the very same problem. Are those prior solutions better than your own? Are they more cost-effective? More easily manufactured? Do those prior inventions have more shelf-appeal? Are they going to be more easily marketed? This is the time to discover and assess your competition, rather than having it splatter in your face after major investments are committed.

Assuming your invention still looks viable, the search also may be useful in identifying corporations with potential for licensing your invention. These will be listed as "assignees" in the bibliographic data on the patent cover page. Once you get the knack of patent searching, you'll find it to be a great pastime for exploring new fields of interest, scanning and reviewing new developments, conjuring further modifications that could be the subject of further invention on your part. You'll learn to reinvent inventions.

Why Focus on Patent Literature? Prior art is, of course, not limited to previously granted patents. It can emerge from any of a wide variety of sources: technology or trade journals, textbooks, magazines, court records, published specifications or diagrams, dictionaries, encyclopedias, technical reports, doctoral theses, the text and illustrations on the back of an old cereal box and so on. The best source for meaningful or pertinent information naturally depends on the nature of your invention. For example, an invention involving a bracket might be readily searched in a hardware catalogue. The USPTO examiner sits among mammoth stacks of trade literature subscribed to for just this purpose.

However, years of institutional experience and a few thoughtful studies point to the patent files as the best place to turn in terms of payback on investment of search effort and time.

A massive and unique resource research both in the United States and abroad indicates that, depending upon the technical field in question, as much as 60% or more of the technology disclosed in patent literature search files cannot be found anywhere else. Expressed another way, the conclusion is that patent files are the exclusive source of most technical information. This is less true in the chemical industry than in the mechanical and electrical fields, because of the highly developed and specialized chemistry-related literature resources that have existed for many years. Another reason for turning to the patent files, as compared to other literature collections, has to do with the sheer volume of these collections and the manner in which the files are organized.

In the United States alone, thousands of newly issued patent documents enter the search files each week. Since a new law took effect in March 2001, thousands of published US patent applications are available for searching, as well. Don't forget that foreign patents and published foreign specifications increase the search load by as much as a million documents every year. Despite differences in national patent systems and, of course, languages, patent literature everywhere presents a similar informational format. And, fortunately, there are useful national and international classification schemes that make document access manageable.

Each US patent application is thoughtfully placed in a technological category for examination. This will be one of more than 400 broad classifications, further subdivided into as many as 300,000 sub-categories. When a patent is eventually granted on the application, its precise classification will be determined based on the invention finally defined by its allowed claims. The principal copy of the granted patent is placed in the "original" classification, and cross-reference copies are designated for other categories depending upon further features disclosed or claimed, or believed by the examiner to be of future search value.

The US Patent Classification System is the most useful of all search tools since it has been repeatedly honed and refined to enhance retrieval of technology disclosures. This is a search aid that should not be overlooked, regardless of the method of search (e.g., manual or electronic). Is it easy to use? No. But, as you'll learn below, use of the USPCS can shave days or even weeks from a rigorous patent search.

Where should you search

Choices to Make

In terms of patent searching, you now know what it is you must do, and why. But, where and how you perform your patent search depends on your personal flexibility and limitations. Do you have time to travel? Would a couple of days in Washington, DC fit into your "vacation" plans? Or, alternatively, would short trips to regional search facilities work better with your personal schedule?

Perhaps your day job or other personal demands permit only late evening keyboard trips to the virtual search rooms of the Internet. Each option holds advantages and drawbacks. It's basically a question of balancing convenience with expectations in terms of thoroughness of search. In any case, you'll come away with valuable information relative to your invention and where it might lead.

The Mother of Search Files

Most would agree that the best place for patent searching is at the USPTO, located in Northern Virginia near Washington, DC. Just a short walking distance from a Metro subway transit stop, you'll find the Public Search Room, or PSR. This facility offers free access to the world's most comprehensive, categorized collection of patent documents. Alternate access through an on-site computerized search system is available, as well - - for a modest fee.

You must bring along a photo identification issued by a government authority (a driver's license will do) in order to obtain a building pass. Other things you should bring along are comfortable clothes and shoes. And you should make sure that accompanying family members have a few bucks for Metro transit passes and a tour map of the Washington-area sites. You'll be here for a while.

Walk around the PSR; scope it out. You'll encounter helpful USPTO staff and scores of professional searchers who make the PSR their operational base. You'll find row upon row of chairs and reading tables, but you'll quickly learn that there are territorial aspects to the facility. It's an informal protocol, but one you must honor. Resident searchers and patent attorneys have staked out certain study zones, and may have used the same chairs and table areas for decades. Strike up a conversation with some of these "locals." They can be helpful in saving you a lot of time in learning the ropes, including where you may want to sit when you do your reading.

The Search Tools

Once you've found your way around the PSR, take a look at the tools of the trade. This is where the US Patent Classification System lives. Voluminous manuals of classification and classification definitions provide a pathway through the stacks of tens of millions of patent documents. However, don't try to use those massive books until you've tackled the Index to US Patent Classification.

This manageable Index is a simple alpha listing of subject matter commonly covered by US Patents. This handy publication, available from the US Government Printing Office, links descriptive terms with categories or classifications. This is where you'll begin to get a handle on the arcane "patentese"- - a descriptive jargon developed over two centuries of Patent Office operation.

Learning the Language

For example, you'll learn that a common nail suddenly becomes a pointed, non-threaded fastener. Crazy as it sounds, there's a good reason for this. The classification scheme is principally based on the function of the inventive device or process. This is an important aspect to keep in mind when you look for your own invention among the millions of documents stored in the PSR.

Once you've found your invention category in the Index, note the associated class/subclass designation (there may be several) which you will use in accessing the Manual of Classification. For example, if you've invented yet another mousetrap, the Index will have shown that animal traps can be found in Class 43. But so are fish and burglar traps. Make a note that the subclass designation for "Animal etc" is 58+, and turn to that designation in the Manual. In the latter, you'll find highly detailed distinctions among animal trap features and functions. If you need a thorough explanation of those distinctions, that's when you turn to the Classification Definitions.

With a sheet of search notes in hand you can then be off to the fee-based computer search terminal or through the labyrinth passageways among endless paper "stacks" to retrieve bundles of patents dating back as far as 1790. Brace yourself for a surprise. There will be thousands of documents in your specific field. It's time to sit down (remembering the seating protocol) and read. Now, here are some very important tips about the use of the paper files.

First of all, you must keep the patent documents in order. These files are used by thousands of people, professionals and non-professionals alike, seeking specific documents and features. Maintaining the order, from oldest (bottom) up to the newest (on top) is not only courteous, but it's also critical.

Second, it's important that you plan to order and pay for copies of patents you want to take with you. You will not walk out of the Public Search Room with even one of the file documents tucked in your boot or anywhere else. People try it every day. The PSR alarms are loud and embarrassing. The Office staff will take your document and your pass, and (worse of all) the resident searchers will laugh at you.

Personal Advice from Examiners

And, here's a bonus tip that will save you a lot of time with the overall process. Once you have learned the classification of your invention, you can use PSR information guides to identify the USPTO Technology Center responsible for handling your Class of interest. Within that area of the Office, you can locate one or more patent examiners whose own day job is to do just what you've been struggling to do in the PSR.

Following the simple step of making a courtesy phone call to check on the availability of an examiner, you can drop by her or his office for advice on specifically where to search for your particular invention. This is not a public disclosure of your invention, and will be held in confidence.

The examiner is not permitted to advise you on whether to file a patent application, though you'll be dying to ask just that. But, you stand to gain a great deal of insight as to where your pre-x search should focus. Most examiners enjoy meeting inventors and talking about the technology that is your common bond, but they have tight time schedules. So you'll have to keep your discussion very brief.

Bonus: Foreign Patents in Classified Order

An added benefit to your visit will be that you can use the examiners' search files to complete your search. (But, be sure to ask first.) These files, located in relatively small search areas near the examiners' offices are essentially mirrored segments of the PSR stacks. But, access in the examiners' search rooms is decidedly easier to manage. And, they include thousands of foreign patents that will make your search even more comprehensive. Rules on maintaining file order and security apply here as well. Also, although you would see that examiners often are at work at all hours of the day and night, the examiners' office areas and adjacent search rooms are closed to the public at 5:00 PM.

There's a Downside

Bringing your search to the greatest technological information collection in the world has a multitude of advantages, but there are shortcomings you should know about. The paper files both in the PSR and the examiners' search rooms are not entirely complete. That is to say that as much as 7 percent or more (depending on the search activity of the field) of the documents are either missing or incorrectly filed. Either way, you won't see a significant number of the patents that should have been there. This is one factor that has driven the electronic search system development

The length of the searching process itself may also come as a shock to the first-time patent searcher. Much time must be committed to identifying the proper subclasses and/or search terms, pulling or downloading scores of documents, reading and rereading the disclosures, and dealing with the massive and confusing infrastructure of a 7000 member USPTO staff.

Typically, a first-time patent search at the USPTO facilities may take at least two full days. Thankfully, there is no shortage of hotels in the surrounding area. *Editor's note: Hotels near the Patent Office are relatively expensive. I found an affordable motel in Alexandria, about six miles south.*

On the other hand, an outstanding, national network of search centers offers an attractive alternative to a USPTO visit. These are called Patent and Trademark Depository Libraries, or PTDL's, and at least one such facility is most likely within minutes or only a couple of hours away.

Patent Searching in Your Own Backyard

New inventors and entrepreneurs are often pleasantly surprised to learn that there are many libraries across the country specially designated and equipped as patent search centers. To be designated as a PTDL, a library must agree to acquire at least a 20-year back file of US patents, and maintain the collection integrity. They are based within government (state, county, city) or university library facilities. There's at least one in every state, the District of Columbia, and Puerto Rico. To find your closest PTDL, you can place a call to 1-800-PTO-9199 or check the USPTO Home Page (www.uspto.gov).

Besides being among the best in the library science field, every PTDL staff member is intensively trained by USPTO personnel. Thus, you'll find these professionals extraordinarily knowledgeable and helpful when it comes to both patent and trademark searching. They have their own networking association ensuring a full sharing of knowledge and best practices. While PTDL staff cannot become directly involved in your search, they stand ready to instruct you as a patron in the use of the PTDL search tools which may range from microform to optical discs and even include the computerized files.

Each of these libraries offers basic patent and trademark electronic searching tools as provided by the USPTO. Some even subscribe to the USPTO's Automated Patent Search System (APS), and a very few are qualified as partnership libraries providing public access, for a fee, to the same comprehensive image and text system utilized by patent examiners in their routine searches.

At the minimum, you'll be able to perform a reasonably complete patent search, albeit very slowly, adopting the typical PTDL's "Seven Step Strategy." This involves the use of CD-ROM or APS text searches to view patent titles in a given Class/subclass, as a step preliminary to collecting listings of pertinent patent numbers. Those patents can then be viewed in whole or part by access to Official Gazettes, microfilm, paper files, APS images or CD-ROM equipment as available.

Some PTDL's include patent search files dating back to the very first US patent grant in 1790. They all maintain a remarkable collection of useful guides and inventor handbooks in addition to a complete set of Official Gazettes, search manuals, patent examination manuals, digests and indexes as are available at the USPTO itself.

Foreign patent collections are not uncommon for PTDL's, and Internet access to a multitude of intellectual property search files, including but not limited to those readily available on the USPTO's Home Page. This, of course, brings us to your most convenient, though somewhat limited access.

Patent Searching at Home

The oft-heard warning, "Do not try this at home," certainly doesn't apply to patent searching. If you're among the many millions with a home-based personal computer, you'll find the world of patent information at your fingertips. A variety of search files exist, some of which even include access to foreign patent literature.

Surfing through any typical Internet search engine will turn up a number of patent file research choices. The USPTO's own Home Page-based files, coupled with the wealth of information to be found on the unique web pages created by the USPTO's Office of Independent Inventors Programs, is a "best bet" for ramping yourself up to electronic searching on your own.

The home-based method is by no means the end-all of searching, as you'll learn below, but searching at your own keyboard can be a great starting point. Besides, you can sit wherever you like.

Electronic Downsides

The quality of a patent search is only as good as the search terms employed, and the searcher's ability to move from point to point in Boolean logic. In other words, some people are darn good at it; others shouldn't trust their results. Another shortcoming that many new to patent searching don't recognize is that text-based electronic search files are limited in years of coverage. In general, text searches only extend back in time to around 1976; generally not far enough to offer a complete search of relevant prior art for many inventions.

Who (really) should perform the search?

Knowing Your Limitations

At some point, regardless of how much searching you have done on your own, you'll arrive at the question: "Should I hire someone to perform a patent search, or should I do it myself? The short answer to that is: "Yes." Opinions may differ, but wisdom dictates that a combination of "hire it" and "do it" works best for most inventors. As discussed above, there are strategic advantages and insight to be gained from attempting your own search. Even if, eventually, you will be engaging the services of a patent attorney or agent, or directly contracting the assistance of a professional searcher, it will help you to know what this search business is all about.

Also, learning as much as you can tolerate about the arcane patent system and the wealth of information that resides in its archives can only help you in your inventive efforts. You'll learn more about your competitors and identify potential licensees of your technology. Besides that, you'll be better able to understand the results brought back to you by those you hire to perform the more comprehensive job of researching your invention.

Finally, as you may have picked up from the very beginning of this chapter, there is another reason for engaging professionals. It has to do with determining if your invention may be considered an "obvious" technological modification. Searching for prior art, with the question of obviousness in mind, is an art in itself.

For example, if your new mousetrap has an automatic flushing feature to wash away the captured creature, a search of mousetraps will not suffice. You'll have to look through the washing and flushing technologies buried in patent collections far removed from the field of vermin traps. And, having finally found flushing systems similar to that employed in your own combination, you'll have to seek out any teaching or suggestion of such combination - - a suggestion, by the way, that may be only inferred in a very subtle way. Suffice it to say, that a thorough and complete search requires great skills beyond what one might learn from a single chapter on searching.

Besides, the product of a patent search, even though remarkably complete (including, of course, the waves of patents and other literature that flow from far beyond USA borders), is not particularly useful to the inventor without an opinion on patentability, one that includes the complex question of obviousness.

Truly useful patent search results will cost money to acquire. They should include an analysis and opinion by a registered patent attorney or agent (listings of whom may be found, by the way, in your local PTDL or on the USPTO Home Page). That opinion should offer sound advice as to what the search has turned up, what the results portend for the patentability of your invention, and the expected scope of coverage (meaning value) to result in any patent that might be forthcoming once your application is filed.

* * *

Patent searching, if you have stamina and patience, if you enjoy the "hunt" and have the time to commit to it, can be interesting and beneficial. But, you must remember that it's also a profession, even an art. It takes great expertise to perform properly and deliver trustworthy outcomes.

* * *

Editor's note: Expect a patent search with analysis and patentability opinion typically to cost between $500 and $1000. It takes time to prepare a well-conceived opinion. Be wary of bargain prices.

Phase 4: Prototyping Your Invention

by Jack Lander
Inventor, author, entrepreneur

Why you must have a prototype

Assuming that your invention is tangible, and can be classified broadly as "hardware," you must have a working prototype in order to conclude a licensing agreement. The odds of selling an idea from drawings and/or a written specification, or from a patent alone, are very poor. Your objective must be to "show and tell" - - to demonstrate the benefits of your invention in a thoroughly convincing way. The perception and reaction of your licensee prospect must be as close as possible to what will be the final consumer's perception and reaction.

Even with an excellent prototype it is often difficult to engage a potential licensee. But without one, you are wishfully dreaming that your prospect will have an exceptional level of imagination, and the insight and patience to use it. This expectation is inconsistent with human nature as it is generally found in the world of business.

Other reasons why you need a prototype

Until you obtain a working prototype, you may not have defined the details that make your invention patentable. Very often the basic invention is not patentable because of prior art, but a detailed feature that provides a *proprietary advantage* over whatever now fills the need becomes the key to a valuable patent.

For example: Suppose that you invent a better mouse trap. It has a unique trigger mechanism that enables anyone to safely set the trigger without risk of springing the trap. Obviously you did not invent the age-old mousetrap; you invented a feature - - its trigger. Subtle features discovered only at the time of prototyping may provide the basis for an otherwise unpatentable or weakly patented invention. A prototype may also reveal features that should be improved and redesigned or even abandoned in order to strengthen your patent.

The ideal prototype

Your prototype should look and operate exactly like the finished product. Every concession from this ideal decreases your chances of eliciting a positive response from your prospect. The more you have to explain and apologize for, the weaker your position and your prospects for an agreement.

If your invention doesn't fit the "hardware smaller than a bird cage" category perfectly, the principles that follow are easily translated for larger items, or items made from materials not covered here. For example, an inventor I know invented a coin-operated ping pong table. This invention is obviously much larger than a bird cage. But all of its components are made from commonly available materials, and manufactured using well-known processes.

Prototypes that are too large or unwieldy to take or send to a prospective licensee can be demonstrated using a virtual prototype. This is an animated CD (compact disk) or videotape. Not only does such animation enable you to demonstrate how your invention works, but you can show internal or normally hidden features.

Virtual prototypes aren't cheap. Animation is a tedious process, even with our lightning-speed computers. But once the initial processing expense is covered, the cost per CD is pocket change, and enables you to demonstrate your invention to a large number of prospective licensees economically by mail.

Virtual prototyping can be used advantageously in conjunction with physical prototypes for large or small inventions. It may be less expenses to produce and send virtual prototypes than to produce and send physical prototypes.

Prototypes vs. pilot runs

A prototype is typically one of a kind - - a substantially hand made model of your invention. A pilot run is a small production quantity made by short-run processes.

A prototype, especially in the early phases of its evolution, is valuable for the inventor's learning, and often requires several iterations before it closely represents the product that eventually will be manufactured and sold.

A final lone prototype is often presented to a prospective licensee. But unless it is prohibitively expensive to do so, a *pilot run* should be produced for such purposes. The main reason is that with only one presentation model, the inventor cannot leave that model with the prospect without crippling his or her parallel efforts to show it to other prospects.

Prospective licensees are typically very slow to make final decisions - - often taking several months to do so. (The detriment of this delay is somewhat off the subject here, but inventors should place time limits on this "meditation" process, and make clear their intention to *negotiate with other prospects* after a certain cutoff date. After that date, any exclusive arrangements will bear a price. For example, give your prospective licensee a one-month exclusive review period with the understanding that beyond that it will cost him or her $1000 a month to maintain the exclusive status, and with a limit of three months - - six months, etc. Without this provision procrastination costs your prospect nothing, but can mean the difference between success and failure to you.)

In the case of presentations to catalog houses - - a marketing channel that is especially attractive to the inventor who intends to manufacture his own invention (or have it contract manufactured for him) - - it is imperative that multiple models be available for submission to several catalogers in parallel. The philosophy of sending out presentation copies in quantity is essential to early success, and especially to avoidance of the discouragement and flagging efforts that often result from serial rejections and a protracted licensing campaign.

The inventor who is not familiar with manufacturing processes often thinks in terms of extremes, that is, that he or she must either make one piece or invest in very expensive production tooling. This is a fallacy. For almost every process there is a *spectrum* of methods, machines, and tooling that are produced economically for a given quantity range. This is a principle that will be explained and discussed in the material that follows. The point here is that the cost of a 25 piece pilot run may only be four or five times that of a single prototype for certain kinds of inventions, and will be affordable if you have budgeted your venture money strategically.

Prototyping principles

By understanding the following key prototyping principles you will be able to make a sound choice of materials and manufacturing processes, and create an effective prototype:

1. Allocate a generous portion of your total project budget to your prototype.

2. Determine the materials and processes that will be used by the eventual licensee to manufacture your invention in the sales volume that you forecast.

3. If you are not well informed about materials and processes, consult a professional product designer who is.

4. Aim basically toward the "big three" processes for high-volume production in order to obtain a quality product at low cost. These are:

    - metal stamping;
    - plastic (or elastomer) molding;
    - die casting.

5. Make your prototypes from short-run processes that produce results nearly identical to the high-volume processes that will eventually be used by the licensee.

6. When you are confident that your next prototype will be the final one, consider producing a pilot run rather

than merely another lone prototype.

7. Solicit manufacturing price quotations in a professional manner.

Principle #1: Budgeting your prototype

If your invention truly has great potential, you cannot afford to skimp on your prototype. Many, if not most, uninitiated inventors fall into this fatal pattern:

1. get great idea.
2. contact patent attorney.
3. react with shock when quoted the price for the patent.
4. scrape together the money and proceed with the patent.
5. fail to consider the costs of prototyping and contacting potential licensees.
7. receive the patent.
8. make several futile attempts to license their invention or find a licensing agent.
9. flounder helplessly (or do nothing) as the patent ages to obsolescence.

Does this sound harsh or cynical? I'm sorry to tell you that it is realistic. The prototype is an essential ingredient in your 'master plan,' and you should consider its cost at the outset.

Principle #2: Determine materials and processes

The closer your presentation model is to its final form as a product for sale, the better your chances of making the desired impression on your prospect. If your invention will be mass marketed, and its major part will be made of plastic, you won't convey an effective image if you present a model that is made of painted balsa wood. Your focus in any meeting with a prospect must be on sales projections, low cost of production, and other business aspects, as well as the functional aspects of the invention. The more your prospect has to bridge the gap between your "balsa wood" model and the final product, the less will be his or her concentration on business aspects.

Now, making your presentation model as I recommend will cost money - - most likely more money than you considered when you started your venture. The compromises you must make along the way are personal and unique to your situation, of course. But that does not alter the principles. Even with a perfect presentation model, you will have discouragements in your quest to license your invention. Don't increase your "rejection quotient" by presenting a jury-rigged model made of inappropriate materials.

Principle #3: Materials and processes

If you don't know which materials and processes are the most appropriate for your prototype, get help. Professional product designers are often very small businesses - - one or two persons - - who design products as free lancers. They can be found in the yellow pages. In my state's "Business to Business (yellow pages) Directory" I find 42 "non bold" listings under "Designers - Industrial." Many of these listings bear the name of an individual, such as, Bob Smith, or Smith Associates, etc. And not one has a display ad, which is a reasonable indication that these are not even medium size firms.

Industrial designers are generally very versatile people. They know which materials and production processes to use in order to achieve good design and low production costs. Many are sympathetic to the struggling inventor, and are willing to provide counsel. The best way to approach them is to ask if they would be willing to spend half an hour or 45 minutes with you on a consultation basis, and ask their hourly fee. This will run anywhere from $50 to $150 an hour - - and probably well worth it. $100 spent with an expert may save you $1000 in false starts.

Make a list of your questions, and don't digress. Your main focus is to determine the materials and processes that your licensee will most likely use in production. Knowing these, your next focus is how to get prototypes made that will look like the eventual product. Get the names of suitable vendors, if possible. In some cases, the designer will have prototyping capabilities that may be suitable.

Principles #4 and #5: Aim toward and emulate the "big three" processes

- metal stamping or drawing;
- plastic or elastomer molding;
- zinc alloy die casting.

Metal Stamping

Your eventual product will be made using production tooling, which generally is very expensive. For example, a stamped metal production tool may cost $10,000+. A plastic component will be made using a plastic injection mold that may cost $15,000+. Obviously, we small inventors cannot afford to have production tooling made in order to emulate the ultimate market-ready product. Fortunately, there is a spectrum of processes that will produce parts that are virtually identical to the full production-tooled parts.

For example, a stamped metal part may be produced economically in very small quantities using laser cutting, or abrasive water jet cutting. Either of these processes will cut out a flat part from sheet metal of any thickness from foil to around 1/2 inch - - even thicker using abrasive water jet. Either of these processes requires a computer program that usually costs less than $100. The parts may cost well under a dollar each. This is an important and universal principle:

> *High-volume processes, such as stamping, molding, and die casting, produce inexpensive parts using very expensive tooling. The opposite is true for prototype processes: The parts are relatively expensive, and the tooling is inexpensive.*

Stamped metal parts are frequently formed (bent) in order to produce brackets, hinges, cabinets, chassis, etc. Forming is often provided by the same vendor that does the cutting.

Plastic injection molding

Injection molding is simply the squirting of molten plastic into a metal mold, cooling it to a solid, and ejecting the completed part. The entire cycle takes half a minute, more or less. As with stamped parts, there are prototyping processes that bypass the expensive mold, and thereby produce relatively expensive parts with inexpensive tooling.

Large parts are often fabricated from sheet and bar stock, which is available off-the-shelf from plastic suppliers. Small parts that are geometrically simple can be machined from bar stock. And parts that are too complex to machine economically can be molded in silicone rubber molds. Fabricated parts are made by plastics fabricators, who are not easy to find. Plastic suppliers, such as Cadillac or AIN, may be able to recommend a fabricator. Plastic parts can be machined at any local machine shop.

Molding in silicone rubber molds requires a master pattern that can be hand carved, machined, fabricated, or made by stereolithography, selective laser sintering, or three-dimensional printing using molten wax. Again, an industrial designer who is a plastics expert can advise you on these processes. Or contact local universities which may offer these services, and free consultation on which of the options is best for your prototyping needs.

Die casting

Die casting is quite similar to plastic injection molding. The temperatures are higher, and the material is zinc alloy or aluminum alloy. And the molds are somewhat more expensive. Simulated die cast parts can be produced in small to medium quantities using investment casting, also called the "lost wax" process.

High strength plastics, such as nylon and acetal, when they are reinforced with short glass fibers are often strong enough to replace die cast parts, and are generally less expensive.

Principle #6: Consider producing a pilot run

In producing small quantities, the cost of setting up for production is usually the main cost. And setup cost is the same whether one, five, or ten (etc.) parts are produced. So, if you are quoted $500 for a prototype, and $300 of that is for setup, this leaves $200 as the cost to perform the machine and hand operations to make the part. Thus, five parts would cost 5 times $200 plus $300 or $1300, an average of $260 each, which is basically one-half as much per unit as the one-piece.

You see the principle here. Prototypes often cost dramatically less per piece in quantity. If a pilot run interests you, be sure to get pricing on various quantities *at the outset,* while the vendor's "pencil is still sharp."

There are, of course, many other manufacturing processes that may be more appropriate for your invention than the big three. If you are in doubt about the best process, don't neglect consulting with an industrial designer. In any event, the principle involved is the same as for the big three: Small quantity processes are available that will make parts that emulate the high-volume production process. These small quantity processes trade low, non-recurring costs, such as tooling, computer programs, etc., for a higher per piece cost, and offer a total cost that is appropriate for prototypes.

Materials

The big three processes covered above dictate the general kinds of materials to be used. Some of the options should be discussed. The stamping process uses mostly cold-rolled steel, and sometimes aluminum, or even stainless steel. Stainless is harder on tools than cold-rolled or aluminum, and is significantly more expensive, both as raw material and in the processing. Stainless is used for medical items, or for items that must endure severe weather.

Most "weatherproof" parts are made from steel, and zinc or nickel electroplated, neither of which give truly permanent protection, but are relatively inexpensive in quantity.

For a few prototype parts, however, electroplating is quite expensive due to the $50 to $75 minimum lot charge that is common. Thus, for prototyping, stainless steel sheet metal or investment castings may represent the least total expense.

Aluminum is often used where weight is a factor. Aluminum has a better strength-to-weight ratio than steel, which is why it is used in aircraft. Aluminum is difficult and expensive to electroplate, however, and is typically "anodized." Anodizing is an electrical process that converts the surface to an inert and particularly hard form of aluminum oxide.

Plastic is a non-technical term for the familiar material. "Polymer" is the correct technical term. Polymers range from fairly inexpensive commercial grades, such as the polyethylenes, to the so-called "engineering polymers," such as acetal, polyimide, and several high-temperature super polymers, etc. Many of the less expensive plastics are known as "thermo-plastics" because they can be remelted. This is an important consideration today due to the emphasis on recycling.

Principle #7: Solicit prototype pricing professionally
The more professional your approach to soliciting prices, the lower the quoted prices will be. Start the process with a few phone calls, and a professionally printed letterhead, envelope, and RFQ (Request for Quotation) form, and after just a bit of practice, you will give the impression of an old timer.

When you first approach the job shop proprietor, he or she is often eager to get your business, and may be concerned about competition. Indeed, the fact that you use a Request for Quotation form conveys the silent message that you are an experienced buyer who probably is soliciting prices from one or two other vendors. At this stage the price quoted may be very fair. But you should *always deal with at least two or three sources.* Even the most sincere job shop proprietor may not be a good manager, or a good estimator, or have the experience and appropriate equipment for your particular job.

However, it is upon *reordering* that you have the greatest risk of paying too much. Here is why: Almost every job produced by a job shop has four key elements in the price. These are:

1. Special tools, fixtures, programs, process plans, shop sketches etc. that are useful the first time the job is run, and *each time it is rerun.* These items go by various names, usually the catchall of "tooling" or NRE (non-recurring engineering).

2. *Setup*. This is analogous to preparing to bake a cake. You must get out each ingredient, the pans, the mixer, etc., and after the cake is baked, you must clean up and put everything away. So, "setup" is the total of all the preparation work that must be done *each time the job is run,* whether you are baking one cake or one hundred. Quite often it merely consists of locating tools, and adjusting the machines for the job at hand, and for short runs it will often take more time than actually running the job.

3. *Running time.* This is the time actually spent in the machining or hand working process.

4. *Learning time.* This is the gained time on each succeeding piece through familiarity, and through discovering shortcuts. What may happen on a rerun of your job is this. Let's say that you first bought one piece, and you are now buying ten pieces:

- The "tooling," no matter how simple or crude, is used again for the rerun. Remember, you already paid for the tooling on your first order.

- Setup is now spread over more units. For example, if the setup was $50, that full amount was charged to your single piece on your first order. The setup assessed to each piece should be $5 on the rerun of 10 pieces.

- Running time per piece will stay about the same as for the first order.

- Learning time will almost certainly result in some shortcuts, or time reduction due to familiarity.

Now here is the way to insure that you get the advantage of these natural time reductions for the larger quantity: *Always ask for a quote on your anticipated larger quantities at the time when you first approach the vendor* for your quote on your single piece. If you buy one or two pieces for prototypes, and then you come back later for the larger quantity pricing, the vendor will imagine that he has the second order "in the bag" - - a sure thing - - and you will have given away your legitimate bargaining advantage.

So, in soliciting a price quotation, you should always indicate the largest quantities that you anticipate purchasing in the future, and ask these questions:

1. What kind of tooling, fixtures, programs, or other non-recurring items will you use in making my prototype?

2. Will this same tooling etc. be used for the larger quantities later?

3. Will I own the tooling? That is, can I pick up the tooling with the job? (Many vendors charge a "tooling charge," which, when worded this way, probably does not give you title to the tooling. The vendor won't release it to you.)

4. Will you supply the raw material, or do you prefer that I supply it?

The first three questions will help keep your vendor honest, and will let him or her know that they aren't dealing with a country bumpkin. The last question may save you a lot of money that the vendor would charge you for the time he would spend in locating and ordering the raw material, especially if it isn't something he is used to working with, such as a small machine shop machining a block of plastic. Also, you have the right to pick up unused raw material when you pick up your parts. If the vendor orders the raw material, he usually considers that the unused portion belongs to him, even though a substantial amount is left over due to having to buy a minimum amount. (Many raw material suppliers charge a $50 minimum, or even higher, and your job shop vendor will end up with much more material than your job requires.)

After you pick up your prototype and work with it, you may wish to make some changes. Be sure to ask to *see* the "tooling" at some time before you make any such changes. This will give you an idea of whether or not your proposed changes will affect the tooling, and whether you will incur new tooling charges.

The Business of Inventing

To save hundreds of dollars in making your prototypes, act like a business. Adopt a business name, and get a letterhead and envelopes made. These days you don't need to buy 500 printed letterheads or envelopes. Copy and print shops like Kinko's and AlphaGraphics have computers on the premises, making it feasible to create a professional looking letterhead and an RFQ form, and even a drawing form, and have just a few printed from a laser printer. If you have your own laser or bubble jet printer, 600 dots per inch or better, then you can do this for yourself, of course.

Drawings

To communicate effectively with any shop that will make your prototype you must submit an "engineering drawing." (Don't let that term scare you. It is just the common title used to distinguish drawings used in manufacturing from other kinds of illustrations, such as drawings used in ads and brochures.)

Today, most professional drawings are made by CAD, "computer assisted design." If you don't have access to CAD, you can find the service listed in the yellow pages under "Draftsmen" (hopefully, "Drafting services" in the future, especially since many CAD operators today are women). But a fancy CAD drawing is not essential. You can use an ordinary #2 pencil and a ruler as long as you provide clear views and the essential dimensions. Each dimension should have a tolerance. For example, if the length of your part is 6 inches, and this is not a critical dimension, you should give the machinist a tolerance of plus or minus 1/32 inch, indicated as 6.00 + or - .03. The application of appropriate tolerances to each dimension is a stronger indication of professionalism than a fancy letterhead or drawing form.

Conclusions

You must have a functional prototype in order to license or sell your invention. Making a prototype that looks as close to the eventual market-ready product as possible is almost certainly more important than saving a few dollars by creating a "painted balsa wood" model.

Don't make the typical mistake made by most uninitiated inventors: Spending all of your money on protection and not having enough to create a first class prototype - - or a pilot run, in the case where a parallel effort must be made, such as submitting to catalog houses, etc.

Use the materials that will most likely be used in the market-ready product, but use the short run processes that avoid astronomical tooling expense. Approach your vendors professionally by using (at the very least) a dimensioned, toleranced drawing, and an RFQ form.

For sources of materials, vendors, and professional help, see the Resources section at the end of this book. To find inventor-friendly prototypers, subscribe to Inventors' Digest magazine through the United Inventors Association.

* * *

Cautionary note: In the third paragraph of this chapter I explained that patentable features may be discovered or invented at the prototyping stage. In your purchase agreement with your prototyper I recommend that you write in a provision that assigns all such features to you without restrictions or compensation beyond the price of the prototype. If such features become the basis for patent claims, your prototyper is a co-inventor, and must be named as such on your patent. Be sure to discuss this point with your patent agent or patent attorney before he or she begins writing your patent application. JL

Phase 5

Patenting Your Invention

by Bob Mason, Esq.
Patent attorney

In understanding what a patent is, it is often useful to review what a patent is not.

Copyrights protect the writings of an author against copying. Literary, dramatic, musical and artistic works are included within the protection of the copyright law, which in some instances also confers performing and recording rights. Copyrights go to the form of expression rather than to the subject matter of the writing, so a copyright to a description of a machine would prevent others from copying the description; it would not prevent others from writing a description of their own or from making and using the machine. Copyrights are registered in the Copyright Office in the Library of Congress.

Trademarks relate to any word, name, symbol or device used in trade to indicate the source or origin of goods and to distinguish them from the goods of others. Trademark rights may prevent others from using confusingly similar marks but not prevent others from making the same goods or from selling them under non-confusing marks. Trademarks (and service marks, for services), which are used in interstate or foreign commerce, may be registered in the Patent and Trademark Office.

Trade secrets are information, e.g., a formula, program, method, or process, that: (1) derives independent economic value from not being generally known and not being readily ascertainable by proper means, and (2) is the subject of reasonable efforts under the circumstances to maintain secrecy. Trade secrets may be maintained indefinitely as long as relative secrecy is maintained. For example, the formula to Coca-

Cola® is a trade secret. No registration or other government action is required to maintain a trade secret.

Patents fall into 3 categories: Plant patents; Design patents; and Utility patents

Plant patents go to anyone who has invented or discovered and asexually reproduced any distinct and new variety of plant, including cultivated sports, mutants, hybrids, and newly found seedlings, other than a tuber-propagated plant or a plant found in an uncultivated state.

Design patents are for new, original and ornamental designs for an article of manufacture, but protects only the appearance of an article, not its structure or utilitarian features. The specification of a design application is short and ordinarily follows a set form. Only one claim is permitted, following a set form. A design patent has a term of 14 years.

When most people consider patents in connection with protecting an invention, they usually refer to utility patents.

Utility patents, or just '**patents**,' are granted on new, useful and non-obvious inventions or discoveries of:

1. Processes (or methods, primarily industrial or technical),
2. Machines,
3. Manufactures (articles which are made),
4. Compositions of matter (chemical mixtures of ingredients, and new chemical compounds), and
5. Improvements in any of the above.

A patent is a property right throughout the United States and its territories granted by the Government, acting through the Patent and Trademark Office. The term of the patent is 20 years from the date the patent is applied for, subject to the payment of maintenance fees. The right is, in the language of the statute and of the grant itself, "the right to exclude others from making, using, or selling" the invention. What is granted is not the right to make, use, or sell, but the right to exclude others from making, using, or selling the invention.

An **application** for a patent is made to the Commissioner of Patents and Trademarks and includes:

1. A written document comprising a specification; (description and claims), and an oath or declaration;

2. A drawing in those cases in which a drawing is necessary; and

3. The filing fee.

The **specification** includes a written description of the invention and of the manner and process of making and using it, and is required to be in such full, clear, concise, and exact terms as to enable any person skilled in the technological area to which the invention pertains, or with which it is most nearly connected, to make and use the same. The specification sets forth the precise invention for which a patent is solicited, in such manner as to distinguish it from other inventions and from what is old. It describes completely a specific embodiment of the invention, and explains the mode of operation or principle whenever applicable. The best mode contemplated by the inventor of carrying out the invention is set forth.

In general, and for most applications, the specification should be arranged as follows:

1. Title of the invention,
2. Brief summary of the invention,
3. Brief description of the several views of the drawing, if there are drawings,
4. Detailed description,

5. Claim or claims, and
6. Abstract of the disclosure.

The *title* of the invention, which should be as short and specific as possible, should appear as a heading on the first page of the specification.

A brief *abstract* of the technical disclosure in the specification must be set forth in a separate page immediately following the claims in a separate paragraph under the heading "Abstract of the Disclosure" and should not exceed 150 words.

A brief *summary* of the invention indicating its nature and substance, which may include a statement of the object(s) or advantage(s) of the invention, commensurate with the invention as claimed and any object recited should precede the detailed description. Such summary should be that of the invention as claimed.

When there are drawings, there shall be a brief description of the several views of the drawings, and the detailed description of the invention shall refer to the different views by specifying the numbers of the figures, and to the different parts by use of reference numerals.

The specification must conclude with one or more *claims* particularly pointing out and distinctly claiming the subject matter which the applicant regards as the invention. The claims are brief descriptions of the subject matter of the invention, eliminating unnecessary details and reciting all essential features necessary to distinguish the invention from what is old. The claims are the operative part of the patent. Novelty and patentability are judged by the claims, and, when a patent is granted, questions of infringement are judged by the courts on the basis of the claims.

The *claim(s)* conform to the invention as set forth in the remainder of the specification and the terms and phrases used in the claims find clear support or antecedent basis in the description so that the meaning of the terms in the claims may be ascertainable by reference to the description.

Once the application is filed with the Patent Office, the terms "patent pending" and "patent applied" *for* may be used to inform the public that an application for patent is on file in the Patent and Trademark Office. The law imposes a fine on those who use these terms falsely to deceive the public.

Applications filed in the Patent and Trademark Office are assigned for examination to the respective examining groups having charge of the areas of technology related to the invention. The examination of the application consists of a study of the application for compliance with the legal requirements and a search through United States patents, prior foreign patent documents which are available in the Patent and Trademark Office, and available literature, to see if the claimed invention is new and unobvious. A decision is reached by the examiner in the light of the study and the result of the search.

The applicant is notified in writing of the examiner's decision by an **action**. The reasons for any adverse action or any objection or requirement are stated in the action and such information or references are given as may be useful in aiding the applicant to judge the propriety of continuing the prosecution of his application. If the invention is not considered patentable subject matter, the claims will be rejected, but the claims may also be rejected if they differ only in an obvious manner from what is found. For inventors not represented by an attorney or agent, examiners are supposed to offer claims for any patentable subject matter disclosed in the application. It is not uncommon for some or all of the claims to be rejected on the first action by the examiner; relatively few applications are allowed as filed.

The applicant requests reconsideration in writing, and distinctly and specifically points out the supposed errors in the examiner's action. The applicant may also **amend**, or change, the claims as long as the changes find support in the specification as filed. In amending an application in response to a rejection, the applicant clearly points out why the amended claims are patentable in view of the state of the art disclosed by the prior references cited or the objections made. The applicant also shows how the claims as amended avoid such references or objections. After response, the application will be reconsidered, and the applicant will be notified if claims are rejected, or objections or requirements made, in the same manner as after the first examination.

On the second or later consideration, the rejection or other action may be made **final**. The applicant's response is then limited to appeal in the case of rejection of any claim and further amendment is restricted.

Interviews with examiners may be arranged, and take place in person or by telephone, but an interview does not normally remove the necessity for response to Office actions within the required time, and the action of the Office is often based on the written record.

As a result of the examination by the Office, patents are granted in the case of about two out of every three applications for patents which are filed.

If the examiner persists in the rejection of any of the claims in an application, or if the rejection has been made final, the applicant may appeal to the **Board of Patent Appeals and Interferences** in the PTO. The Board of Patent Appeals and Interferences consists of the Commissioner of Patents and Trademarks, the Deputy Commissioner, the Assistant Commissioners, and the examiners-in-chief, but normally each appeal is heard by only three members. An appeal fee is required and the applicant must file a brief to support his/her position. An oral hearing will be held if requested upon payment of the specified fee.

As an alternative to appeal, in situations where an applicant desires consideration of different claims or further evidence, a new continuation application is often filed. The new application requires a filing fee and should submit the claims and evidence of which consideration is desired. If it is filed before expiration of the period for appeal and specific reference is made therein to the earlier application, the applicant will be entitled to the earlier filing date for subject matter common to both applications.

If the decision of the Board of Patent Appeals and Interferences is still adverse to the applicant, an appeal may be taken to the Court of Appeals for the Federal Circuit or a civil action may be filed against the Commissioner in the United States District Court for the District of Columbia.

If, on examination of the application, or at a later stage during the reconsideration of the application, the patent application is found to be allowable, a *notice of allowance* will be sent, and a fee for issuing the patent is due.

Occasionally two or more applications are filed by different inventors claiming substantially the same patentable invention. The patent can only be granted to one of them, and a proceeding known as an interference is instituted by the Office to determine who is the first inventor and entitled to the patent. About one percent of the applications filed become involved in an interference proceeding.

Each party to such a proceeding must submit evidence of facts proving when the invention was made. In view of the necessity of proving the various facts and circumstances concerning the making of the invention during an interference, inventors must be able to produce evidence to do this. If no evidence is submitted, a party is restricted to the date of filing the application as his earliest date. From the decision of the board of Patent Appeals and Interferences, the losing party may appeal to the Court of Appeals for the Federal Circuit or file a civil action against the winning party in the appropriate United States district court.

Provisional patent applications

Provisional patent applications are intended to be simple and inexpensive. No claims are needed, no oath or declaration is needed, and the filing fee is lessened. A provisional application, however, will never issue as a patent. In fact, a provisional application will never be examined in the same way as a regular patent application, and it will automatically go abandoned twelve months after it is filed. What a provisional application provides is a U.S. priority date for a subsequently-filed U.S. or foreign application, and it does so without counting against the term of any resulting patent.

The four basic requirements of a provisional application follow:

1. The name(s) of the inventor(s);

2. A specification substantially the same as a non-provisional, except for claims;

3. Drawings, if necessary to understand the invention;

4. And a fee of $150 ($75 for small entities) currently.

In addition to the above, PTO rules require a cover sheet to be filed with the application that identifies the application as a provisional application, and lists the inventor(s) of the disclosed subject matter and his or her (their) residence(s), and the title of the invention.

If the cover sheet fails to identify the application as a provisional application, the application will be treated as a "regular" application. This may have significant consequences because a "regular" application will be incomplete without at least one claim, and it will not receive a filing date.

There are many factors to consider in deciding whether to file a provisional application, making any kind of simple litmus test unrealistic. Advantages to filing a provisional application include a lower initial filing fee, the opportunity for an early filing date without starting the 20-year patent term, and a one-year deferral of the time and expense of prosecuting the patent application. One note of caution is that filing a provisional application starts the one-year Paris Convention Treaty period for filing foreign applications. Thus, at the end of the twelve month period, applicant(s) will not only have to file a regular U.S. application, but must also file all desired foreign applications.

* * *

Editor's note regarding the practical side of foreign patents.

To cover Japan and the principle countries of Europe is generally prohibitively expensive for the inventor of average means. And as with all patent protection, the inventor can be victimized by unscrupulous parties who intentionally infringe his or her rights. The expense of aggressive litigation against a United States infringer often exceeds one million dollars. To litigate overseas may cost even more, and the difficulties are compounded by travel expenses, foreign language communication, and foreign laws and lawyers.

There are three practical strategies for dealing with foreign patents:

1) *license your patent quickly, before the grace period for foreign filing expires, and shift the burden of expense to the licensee. (The grace period is one year from the date of filing your U.S. patent, but the practical period would be more like ten months in order to allow your licensee time to prepare an application and file.)*

2) *Engage a financial partner to take over the cost. Financial partners seldom are interested in licensing deals. But if you put together a management team that will*

start a company based on your invention, your investor may invest in foreign patents. Most 'angels' are generally interested in startups that are based on medical or high-tech products with eventual public stock-offering potential. (More in Appendix B on Financing.)

3) *abstain from filing, and let overseas copycats have their day. This decision should be based on practical economics, not on anger or the need to win. This isn't football.*

I'm sure you already know that a foreign producer of your invention cannot export it to the United States. Legal efforts to stop imports are more practical and far less expensive than infringement litigation conducted overseas.

* * *

Phase 6a

Finding the Markets for Your Invention

by Jeffrey Dobkin
Author and entrepreneur

Editor's note: This chapter is essential whether you intend to license or produce your invention. If you plan to license, whether you search for a licensee yourself, or delegate this to an agent, you must know the markets through which your invention can be sold in order to maximize your contacts. If you plan to produce your invention, again, you should consider all of the markets in which it can be sold.

Have a new idea or new product? Here's how to find the markets for your invention, and what to do when you find them.

But before I show you how easy it is, and the best tools available to find your markets, take a piece of paper and write down all the markets to which you think your product or invention would sell. A market is any group of people you can define that has the potential to buy your product. Narrow it down as tightly as you can. This is step one: Figure out exactly what group or groups are the most likely to need, want, and be able to purchase your product. You've got to define exactly who your market is before you're able to figure out how to reach it.

The tighter the specifications to find your markets, the lower your marketing costs will be. If you are selling books to middle school teachers, most of your money will be wasted if you advertise to all teachers. Your market is teachers, grades 7 through 10. Any material you send to anyone else just shows up on the red side of your balance sheet under "expenses."

Let's take a few examples. Your task would be simple if you

developed a new camera lens for Canon's line of professional cameras. Find a list of all the owners of Canon professional cameras and you've done all the homework you need to do —you've just found your entire market. Your advertising would have no wasted expense when you mail to them, because every person in that list is a potential buyer for your lens.

If this list isn't available (and a list this tightly qualified usually isn't), your market could be found in the readership of several magazines whose subscribers are a group of people defined as Professional Photographers. Although there is some wasted expense in advertising to this group, it is still pretty easy to find this target market.

Suppose you've invented a new tripod to hold any type or brand of camera. Here, your task of finding the specific markets—groups of prospects most likely to purchase your product—is more complex. Surely if your tripod is of good quality, the professional photographers market is a good place to start. But how about the consumer photographic market?

The consumer market is much broader, as well as a little more elusive to reach: Consumers don't all read the same dozen or so photography trade magazines the pros read. Since there are a large number of consumers you must reach with the message that your new tripod is available, it's vastly more expensive. Still, sales can be brisk, and you can make big money with a consumer product if you're good, and focus tightly on the camera market. Camera? Focus?

Maybe your tripod could also be sold to the video camera market, which is a totally different group of professionals and consumers, who own a different classification of products, who need your tripod. These folks read a totally different group of magazines and shop in vastly different stores and catalogs.

But these folks, these video camera owners, have a lot of

money. Now you're going to have to choose which market is better for tripod sales. Who are the more likely users, or better yet, the more likely purchasers?

How about sales of your tripods to back yard astronomers to mount their telescopes? Or how about selling to the security market, where people need sturdy stands for surveillance cameras? Or, how about . . . well, you get the idea. These are all separate and distinctly different markets. All the people in these markets can be reached through the magazines they read, but each group reads a completely different set of magazines. Now you're learning about the finesse of marketing. Think about all the market niches where your products would sell. In a minute you'll see how to reach them.

Take another example. For a while I owned a company that manufactured I.D. tags. It wasn't too exciting, but we did some nice numbers—we placed about 25,000 pounds of mail a year into the mailstream. For a quick study of in-depth marketing, take a one-minute look at where we marketed our I.D. tags.

First, the pet industry was a big market for us - - we marketed pet I.D. tags to the owners of 54 million dogs and 57 million cats, give or take a few million. In a completely separate industry, we made emergency medical I.D. - - personalized identification bracelets and neck pendants for the medical community, specifically for the sub-specialty markets of people with diabetes and people taking heart medication.

To the child care industry, we sold I.D. tags to parents, to lace onto their child's sneaker so young children would have some sort of identification on them. To the running industry, we sold them as runners' sneaker identification tags. We marketed through runners' magazines and through directors of race marathons.

Besides these industries, we marketed our product to laboratories and laboratory equipment manufacturers as permanent, indestructible name plates for equipment.

To the machinery industry, we marketed the same product as valve tags; to the luggage industry, as baggage tags; and to golf bag manufacturers and through golf and pro shops, as golf bag identification. To the woodworking industry, we personalized plaques for woodworkers' custom cabinetry and hobbyists' handmade wood projects. To zoos, we marketed our I.D. tags as name plates for animal cages; to the equestrian industry, as horse halter, tack, and saddle identification tags.

To medical and veterinary doctors, we marketed the same I.D. tags as identification tags for their stethoscopes; to art museums, for photo and picture nameplates; and to the commercial fishing industry, as identification tags for lobster and crab pots—as required by law. So what other markets did you say your product fit into? By the way, we manufactured only five shapes of tags and offered only one style of engraving. Here's the Plan:

Think of all the markets where your product can be sold, then rank them—starting with your primary market as number one. Exactly what groups of people will be most likely to buy your product? As you can see from the examples, if you came up with only one group, you can probably go back and find several more.

Figure out all your markets, then find all the magazines that go to these markets; then, finally, create and send a press release to all those magazines. A press release is a one page document you send to magazines describing your product and its benefits. The magazine then publishes it for free. Simple plan, isn't it?

From the response you receive from your press releases, you'll be able to see exactly which markets have the most interest in your product. If you're not familiar with writing for the press, see the article in my book, *How to Market a Product for Under $500* on writing press releases (available through the UIA web site at www.uiausa.org) and read the first chapter - - almost fifty pages - - on writing press releases and how to submit them with the best possible chance of having them published.

Step II—Finding Your Markets

There are several great reference books found in most libraries that list all markets and the magazines that are sent to each. All the reference tools are easy to use, and you will be able to use them after this five-minute introduction.

The main players are the directories of magazines. Big, thick, 1,000- to 1,500-page books of easy-to-use information. The best ones are Burrelle's Media Directory/Magazines and Newsletters, Bacon's Newspaper/Magazine Directory, the Oxbridge Communications National Directory of Magazines (also their National Directory of News-letters and the Standard Periodical Directory), and the SRDS (formerly Standard Rate and Data Service but now officially called by just their acronym) Business Publication Advertising Source™.

Each of these directories has a similar setup, with easy-to use features. Why do I say they're easy to use? In the front of each book the publishers have a single page of instructions. From this you can understand that using these marketing tools is quite easy—quite a contrast to using your VCR, for which you received a 30-page instruction manual! All the directories group the entire universe of people into about 90 to 110 distinct markets or industries, and they're all listed alphabetically by subject in the market classification section: two or three pages that are found in the front of each book. How convenient. If you can remember the alphabet, you can perform the marketing function.

Examples of industries you can look up would include everything from accounting, banking, fire fighting, or heating, to tourism, veterinary, or woodworking, to name just a few. Any profession or industry you can think of has one or more magazines published for it, and larger industries may be served by hundreds of magazines. All the industries and markets and all their accompanying magazines are listed in these directories.

For example: If you were marketing a product to the motorcycle industry, you'd pick any directory and look up "M" for "Motorcycles" in the market classification section. Then you'd turn to the main section of the book—the magazine data section—where all the motorcycle magazines are found in a single location under "M" for motorcycles. There you'd see all 38 magazines sent to the motorcycle industry, along with their data: circulation, ad costs, publisher, phone and fax numbers, and other miscellaneous information.

Another way to use these books to find the markets you're researching (and the magazines that serve them) is to know the name of any one magazine sent to that particular industry. Each reference book has an alphabetical title directory; if you know the title of a magazine, look it up there.

While American Photographer would be listed under "photography" in the market classification section, in the title index you'd look under "A" for American, and scan down to American Photographer. The directories then show you the page in the magazine data section where the magazine is found. Turn to that page and, lo and behold, American Photographer is grouped with all the other photographic magazines.

Fast and easy; and you thought marketing was hard. Nope. Just time consuming; some industries have dozens of specialty magazines, and the lucrative markets have even more.

While the lawn and garden supplies industry may have only a dozen magazines, the computer industry has over 450 magazines that go to every niche of the computer market. Man, those computer geeks must like to read. But you don't have to worry about reading all of the magazines now. You only have to read them if you're going to place an ad in one. Right now, you're just going to explore the markets with press releases.

Finding a single market would take you about five minutes, if you're a slow reader. Once you've found the markets you're prospecting to, and you see all the magazines sent to those industries, you'll have a pretty good idea of how you can reach your prospective buyers through those magazines, and of how large each market is.

Here's an optional step, but I recommend it. If you think your product will really fit in well in a particular magazine, call the magazine publisher and ask for a media kit. It's free. Ask for a couple of recent samples of their magazine, too. Media kits contain the magazine's ad rates and are always sent free to potential advertisers. If you'd like to get the annual directory the magazine publishes, ask for a sample of that, too.

There's never a charge for any of this material if they think you're serious about advertising. If the directory is normally expensive, here's your chance to get it free, by mentioning how you may take out an ad in it and would appreciate a sample copy for evaluation. This is also a great way to get the directory if it's published at a different time of the year and is no longer attainable through normal channels.

If you don't want to call, you can also write to the publishers and ask for a media kit. Use business stationery so they know you're a serious player and have the money to place an ad. The magazine publishers are pretty good about getting their promotional material right out—it means revenue to them to have an ad come in, so they strike while the lead is hot.

The media kit contains all the hype about the magazine and why you should spend all of your advertising money in that publication. All kinds of information about the industry are also included. While most of this package is usually fiction, there are always some industry insights that will help you with your marketing.

Now that you've found the magazines that serve the industries compatible with your product, create a press release and cover letter and send them to the magazines with a photo of the product. In about three months you'll start to receive inquiries from the readers of the magazines who saw your published press release and are interested. Good luck.

* * *

Phase 6b

Licensing Your Invention

by Lisa V. Lloyd
Successful inventor

To succeed in licensing, your invention should be patented or, at least, patent pending. Unless you are well known in your field, licensing an unprotected invention is very difficult.

Licensing is giving someone else the right to make, to use, and/or to sell your invention. You can give that right to them a number of ways, but it's only with your permission that they have the right to go ahead and make it, use it, or sell it. For example, if you go to the store and purchase any of my patented products, you just purchased the right to use them. On the other hand, manufacturers like Scunci, and Goody, pay me for the right to make and sell my inventions. It is these kinds of manufacturers that we all are looking for.

How do you find these people? For starters, if your invention is destined to be a consumer product, you should go to the stores that are likely to sell similar products. Take a notebook and a pen with you. If it is a tool, you might go to Sears, to Home Depot, and to Ace Hardware. I usually visit three different stores. Large chains are preferred over locally owned retailers because they can expose your product to masses of potential buyers. Go into the department where your product would most likely be sold, and look at who's selling products related to yours. Look at the packaging of lines your product would fit nicely into, and write down the names of the manufacturers, their addresses, etc. Call them or go to their web sites. That's how you can build a list of potential licensees.

The reason I urge you to go to several stores is because different stores carry different brands of the same or similar products. In the hair-accessories business, Goody is dominant in some stores, and nonexistent in others. So, the stores are where we start.

The reference section of the public library is another place where you can find information on manufacturers. It has a variety of directories. One of the most useful, the *Thomas Register of American Manufacturers,* can be found online, too. Sometimes you can find a licensing manufacturer that way.

And there are countless trade publications devoted to all sorts of industries. If you identify the applicable SIC (Standard Industrial Classification) code for your product, you can find the companies that manufacture the same kind of product as yours. Note: SIC codes are now known as NAICS codes (North American Industrial Classification System). This system, developed jointly for the U.S., Canadian, and Mexican governments, assigns a code to each kind of product. Such code can be searched manually in reference books, or through a computer search service to which your library may subscribe. Ask your reference librarian about looking up the NAICS number for your product, and then searching for companies that produce the same kind of product. Also, consider complementary product lines. A smug mousetrap manufacturer may have no interest in your novel mouse trap, but a rat poison manufacturer who has no trap products may be very interested.

This is not, however, one of my favorite ways because it is impossible to tell who is a contract manufacturer (also known as a 'job shop') and who is a licensing manufacturer. It is the long way around, but good to know about.

Trade shows may also be helpful. Be cautious about attending such shows that are specifically for inventors. There are only two or three in the country that really get the kind of turnout from buyers and decision makers that we would hope to meet at these shows. You're better off spending your money to attend, not exhibit, shows that focus on your field or target industry such as gourmet foods, automotive accessories, health and beauty or whatever. This is especially true if you're operating on limited funds, as most of us usually do in the beginning. In most cases, you'll want to select the one or two biggest shows in the country.

Before you go to a trade show or otherwise take your invention out in public, I would strongly advise you to have a patent pending. It doesn't have to have issued, necessarily. But as soon as you go to a show and you offer your creation, you are making public notice of the fact that it exists. From that date, you have one year to file a patent. The clock starts running. Furthermore, someone could steal it if you haven't filed for a patent. Even if you invented it three years ago, and you can prove you invented it first, you're still stuck with having to take them to court to get your money out of them. You don't want to find yourself in that situation. If the bad guys have deeper pockets than you do, they win. It's a sad fact that, in legal conflicts, you only get as much justice as you can afford.

You should also know about licensing agents. They seem to be more numerous now than when I first began inventing. This is probably a response to a significant increase in the number of independent inventors. We are part of what has become, in the last five years or so, an international business. It's amazing. And where there's business activity, there are solicitors. You can find these agents by reviewing past and current issues of *Inventors' Digest* magazine. You will find several listed. The editor and publisher of *Inventors' Digest,* Joanne Hayes-Rines, does not accept ads from agents with questionable ethics. Many charge up-front fees. In addition, there's an organization called LES, the Licensing Executive Society. They specialize in technology. If you have a simple widget they're probably not going to be much help. They would like to be able to help more people with widgets, but they can't get people with widgets to join, so they don't attract the agents who are looking for widgets to license. And then there is Invention University. We aren't agents. We try to help people do everything that an agent would do, but with an emphasis on training you to do things for yourself. We teach a process and you're taking the responsibility and keeping a larger share of your eventual profits. Agents usually charge a fee in advance, and a percentage of the proceeds from the licensing agreement. Occasionally, the really good agents will just take a percentage, but they're hard to find, and they're very selective about which products they choose to represent. In my opinion, it's just as hard to get them to take on your product, as it is to go straight to the companies yourself. Invention University helps you prepare all of the information that you need to pursue those companies without incurring the costs associated with an agent's services using the same techniques I am telling you about today.

Now, what are manufacturers looking for? Put yourself in the manufacturer's position, and try to think about your invention from their point of view. Obviously, profitability is going to be the ultimate issue for them. That's why knowing your numbers from the very beginning is so important. The very first questions they ask may have to do with costs and potential profits. What does it cost to make? What are the competitive prices? Basically, you need to know in advance what's in it for them. You hope to have some notion of their market share - - who they are, and where they stand in the market? What can your product do to increase their share of market?

Manufacturers have told me, "Don't send people to us until they know our company." It's amazing. So know their market share and how your product might help. In some situations, these are extremely difficult or impossible goals. For example, I wasn't able to nail down hard numbers for the industry with the French Twister. What I could do was take a look at similar accessories and what kind of penetration they had in the market. How much money was being spent on those types of accessories? What did the typical unit costs look like? I researched the Topsy Tail at the library. I found several articles that mentioned numbers that I could use as a reference for my product.

Also, ask yourself, is your invention a natural fit with their existing product line? Will they be able to take advantage of established channels of distribution? Is it compatible with their marketing programs? Take note, these are all items to list in your presentation to your prospect.

Efficiency is another major issue for licensing prospects. That is, it is either more efficient to make or sell, or it is more efficient to their customers than its nearest competitor. It was a big deal with one of my licensees when I showed them how they could make the product in the United States. Previously, the competitive product could only be made overseas, because it incorporated a spring. The labor involved in assembling it was prohibitively expensive in this country. My design had no spring, so the labor cost of the existing design was eliminated. The licensee could make my design right here in its own manufacturing plant, and match the price of the imported product. They could mark it "Made in the USA," which Wal-Mart likes, which consumers like, which union members like, and so on. That's competitive structure; that's what mattered to them. That was probably the biggest selling point.

The costs of commercialization and the investment required to manufacture the invention matters greatly. What are they going to have to spend? That's why, where appropriate, you need to include any numbers you can develop on the tooling price and the part price in the package. They should have those numbers right up front. This is what it's going to take for you to be in business on this product. That's important, and it shows efficiency.

It is absolutely your responsibility to know these types of things about the companies that you call on. The more you know about the company, the more likely its managers are to take your proposals seriously. So it's up to you to do your homework and make sure that you understand who you are trying to do business with. Is their stock publicly traded? If so, get a copy of their annual report. If they're privately held, what kind of sales numbers did they post last year? What has their growth rate been in recent years? And so on.

Okay, so now you've found them. You've made your list, you know what kind of sales they have... how many employees they have and you have a realistic idea of what the market potential is for your product within each company. How do you communicate with them? More importantly, how do you negotiate with them? Actually, you may be surprised by how quickly you can move toward your goal if you don't insist on doing the complicated thing - - if you try to keep moving in a straight line. How about this for a stroke of genius? You give them a call and ask, "Do you accept outside invention submissions or new product submissions from independent inventors?"* That's not real hard. And the answer will be either "yes" or "no." If they say "yes," then you ask them to explain their policy. And take good notes.

**Editor's note: Many experienced inventors and professionals advise against identifying yourself as an inventor, and prefer using the title, 'new-product developer.'*

Some companies will refer you to a prerecorded message, because they get so many calls. Or sometimes they'll say, "We have a package that we need to send to you." They'll ask for a mailing address. And when their package arrives, you'll open it to discover their version of a non-disclosure form. They want you to sign their form that says, basically, you promise not to sue them if they already have a design or a product similar to yours. They do this in self-defense, because we live in the world's most litigious society, and people have sued them so many times that the only way they can continue to review outside products at all is if people promise not to sue them. They have their own R & D guys in the back room. It's quite possible they're thinking up the same thing at the same time and they don't want you to sue them over it. Now that doesn't mean that if they really broke the law, or violated your rights, you can't sue them. Their agreement doesn't protect them if they act in an illegal manner.

If they tell you that they don't have any particular policy, but they'd like to take a look at what you have, you would ask them to sign *your* non-disclosure form. Fax it to them, and as soon as they sign it and send it back to you, you can put a package in the mail. You should also send it registered or certified mail for proof of when and where you sent it. The contents of the package will depend on what the manufacturer requires and what you can put together in the way of documents, photographs, drawings, descriptive language and such. I like to prepare a hot sheet (also known as a 'sell sheet') similar to the one we illustrate for catalogs. I prefer to keep it to one sheet, because you only have a moment or two to catch their attention. It should tell the manufacturer "what's in it for them" as we mentioned before as well as what's in it for their customer. Make sure when you're doing this, that you're completely factual and honest. This one sheet has one function and one function only; it is designed to get the prospect interested enough to pick up the phone and ask for more information. It should not be designed to completely sell the product, just sell them on the idea of wanting to find out more about it. Sometimes a short video or compact disk can accomplish the same thing. When I presented the Weave N Wave, a video was all it took, no words, just music and a quick demo. Some people tend to jump the gun and behave as though they are negotiating at this point. But not yet, that's still to come.

So...on that much-anticipated day when someone finally does call and ask for more information what do you say? Please don't lose it here. There is absolutely nothing wrong with saying this is your first time doing this, and then start firing off questions. You could say, "I'm really not sure of what to expect, can you tell me a little bit about what you've done with other inventors?" People often tend to lose integrity when they start talking about money. Even the best of people may start to drift a little bit, ethically speaking, because they're nervous and they feel insecure. They have the sense that they're in a risky situation. They are afraid of losing that one, enormous opportunity. The very best thing you can ever do, to give yourself peace of mind when you're talking to potential licensees, is to be absolutely straightforward. So make sure you're honest. The people on the other side will generally respect that. You also want to make sure your conduct and your manner of speaking are professional. Don't be too casual with them. Avoid using slang or profanity. You want to be taken seriously, so you need to behave like a serious adult, no matter how the other person is speaking to you.

When you're talking to prospective manufacturers, you need to employ a technique that every successful salesperson knows and uses constantly. You need to ask lots of questions. Questions do two things for you. First, when you are asking the questions, you control the direction and content of the conversation. Second, the answers the other person gives to your questions will tell you what's important to them. Questions enable you to identify critical issues, major motivators and hot buttons. The only way to effectively sell them on your invention is to know what they are looking for, so you can present what you have in a way that meets their needs.

The communication process here is similar to taking a test in school. You wouldn't expect a good grade if the teacher kept the questions a deep, dark secret. And you can't expect to make a powerful impression on a manufacturer unless you make your invention fit their perceived needs. So ask them questions. Find out what their needs are. And then make sure you address those requirements that your invention satisfies. You can do this and still maintain the utmost integrity. Usually, what you do is emphasize certain features or benefits more than others based on what they've told you they want.

The prestige of the development can be a significant consideration. When I first approached one of the potential licensees with Soft Claws, I made a big mistake. I hadn't really figured out the product. I wasn't prepared to represent its flexibility in terms of variations and different styles. I had only made one version. They rejected the product, which they probably wouldn't have done if it had been fully developed. They couldn't see beyond the very limited picture that I was showing them. I hadn't done my job. They were properly absorbed with running and building their business. So not only could they not see other fashion opportunities in the product, but they also couldn't see having to do all of the due diligence that still needed to be done -- what it was going to cost to tool up and make the product. I had short-changed myself, because I hadn't bothered with any of it. I had a price for the mold, based on a contingency agreement, but that was meaningless. It wasn't a real world number that could be plugged into the manufacturer's operation.

The competitive advantage offered by your product may be a large factor. The design may have a dramatic effect on the profit margins available from the product. We're talking about the spreads between cost and wholesale and retail. Let's say you have a product, and your competitive analysis tells you it could retail for $11.99. You also know that it will cost $2.10 to produce. If the wholesale price is typically half of the retail price, that's $6.00. So, instead of making the normal three dollars, they're going to make almost four dollars. That's a substantial increase in the expected profit margin. That's a good thing. Manufacturers are impressed by such numbers.

The scope of the innovation is another significant factor in your negotiations. "Me-too" products are not something companies are interested in. Imitation may be the sincerest form of flattery, but it rarely serves as the basis for high-dollar licensing deals. So what can you do if you have an idea that's an improvement on something that's already out there. We talked about it on the patenting side; let's talk about it on the licensing side. A "me-too" product is something that basically does the same thing a different way. And it probably would sell for about the same price. There's nothing significantly different about it other than the fact that the inventor found another one of the numerous ways to solve a given problem. You may have been able to get a patent on it, but most companies won't be interested in it, and neither will the buyers at the stores. So it's very hard to sell. That's not to say it can't be sold; just that it's very difficult. That's a battle I choose not to fight.

If you do decide to work with a "me-too" product, you'd better be looking for things that are going to give it a unique and truly striking advantage, something that will definitely set it apart from the existing product. One example would be a product with identical features and benefits that cost 50% less that the existing competition. That's a big difference. That really sets it apart. That's the scope of its innovation.

It's vitally important for you to appreciate and understand these considerations now. You'll be able to make them a regular part of the inventing process. You can make creative decisions all along the way that will strengthen your position when you start searching for a licensee. And you won't lock yourself in to a product and a patent that incorporate characteristics that are fatal from the manufacturer's point of view. I can't stress this too heavily: The seemingly minor choices when you are in the early stages of the inventing process can have enormous consequences when you try to take it to market. You can build overwhelmingly attractive advantages into your invention, or you can design it to fail miserably, and the functional characteristics can be identical.

As the conversation turns from interest to actual negotiations, there are several factors that both parties should be considering for discussion. We'll start with the three most common: Up Front Amount; Guaranteed Minimum; and a Fair percentage. Most companies want an exclusive agreement, at least in their industry. An example is that of the inventor of a new light bulb. The inventor has entered into an exclusive license for the mortuary industry. The light bulb gives the appearance of a candle flame when you put it inside frosted glass. Mortuaries are big on having candles, and lots of people will go and put them up next to their loved ones. But the licensee only got an exclusive for selling the bulbs to funeral homes.

Next he'll pursue outdoor lighting opportunities, Malibu lighting and applications of that kind, then maybe Christmas lights. Each of those manufacturers would all be a separate, exclusive agreement, because they target totally different markets; they're really not competing with each other. I haven't seen a non-exclusive with a large company yet.

That brings us to our first point, an up-front amount. Most of the time, the up-front amount is in consideration of what you've put into the invention up to that point. On my first invention, I told the manufacturer, during our negotiations, that I had invested $20,000, so that's what they paid me for an advance. It turned out I had $50,000 in it. The lesson is: Keep good records, and do the math. Up-front money is often an advance on future royalties, and comes back out of your own money, in effect, rather than being a bonus in addition to royalties. So that makes that number fairly arbitrary. Just remember, if it is credited towards future royalties, you may not get another check for a long time, so be careful what you ask for.

You should also request a guaranteed minimum periodic dollar amount, regardless of eventual sales volume. The minimum amount is to assure you that the company won't take your product and shelve it for any of several reasons. And if they do, you don't care too much, because you're getting what you agreed on, and it was obviously an amount that you were comfortable with.

Then you have to agree upon a fair royalty percentage. This percentage hopefully will net you payments that are over and above the guaranteed minimum. The royalty may vary from about three to eight percent on your standard widgets, with five percent being the most common.

The final written agreement should include definitions of terms. These will vary, but are a necessity. People ask me if I have contracts that I can show them. The fact is, they're all so different, there's just no standard; and comparing them would be a waste of time. Conversely, within a given industry, the standard trade practices may be such that a contract from Company A looks like it was copied from Company B. The agreement with the company that purchased the rights to sell that light bulb into the mortuary business was one of the worst written contracts I've ever seen. It looked like the licensee had spent about five minutes writing it. Another company, dealing with the same invention, might have dropped six pounds of legalese on the inventor. It really just depends on the size of the business, the professionalism of the company, and their experience in licensing. If you license to a company that's only licensed two or three products from anybody, then they may not be as definite and comprehensive as someone who does it all the time.

You always want to see a section entitled "definitions." It breaks down the words that are going to be used in the agreement, and it is very important. For example, the licensee may use the term "licensed invention" in quotes throughout the contract. On the face of it, that's simple enough. Yet in the definitions, "licensed invention" may be defined by one patent number, but what if it's the wrong number, or a variation of your invention is covered by a second patent? The definition of the term "net sales" may greatly influence the size of your earthly fortune by the way it is defined. And you can believe me when I tell you that "net sales" means wildly different things, depending on who happens to be writing the definition. As a general rule, from what I've seen in my experience, the net is the wholesale, minus commissions, freight, discounts and returns. They don't deduct utilities or the secretaries' salaries or the cost of bottled water, but that doesn't mean someone won't try to diminish your royalties by engaging in weird wording.

Pay close attention to the timing of payments and the representations and warranties. Whether you do so or not, the licensee will do so. Then there's termination. I've not seen one licensing agreement yet that didn't have a termination clause that allows the manufacturer to get out of the agreement; whether or not they include a termination clause is arguable. One of my licensed manufacturers could, at any point, decide that the product is not doing well enough for them, and give notice of cancellation, and that's it, we're done, even though the length of our agreement is for twenty years.

I hope this section has been most helpful for you. I am very proud to have enjoyed the great successes I've had licensing. They've been the most nerve-racking yet exhilarating experience of my life! If you are anything like me, you probably have lots of ideas floating around in the back of your head. The good news is, it gets easier! Learn from this book. Learn from your experiences and grow. I've heard it said, "The definition of insanity is doing the same thing over and over expecting a different result." If that's true, then don't be a crazy inventor. Try everything, and if one way doesn't work, try another until you get the result you are looking for.

In review, do your journal. Perform your due diligence. Due diligence answers what will it cost to make, what will it cost to sell and what will people pay for it? Is it on any of the patent search web sites? Is it being sold somewhere on the Internet? Remember, you don't have to have a patent to sell it, but if someone's selling it somewhere, then you're not the inventor, so you can't get a patent, either. You need to search all over, including the stores. That's all part of your due diligence.

Once you get through that part, you can begin to really refine your invention. That may mean it stays the same and you're just cleaning it up ergonomically - - or you need the services of an engineer to produce drawings to scale and a working prototype, but here is where you start to spend the real money. And then finally you apply for a patent: design, utility or provisional, depending on your strategy. While the attorney or agent is preparing your application, you can start your actual business plan. You may be planning for a full scale business, you may be planning for a beta test to ultimately license, or, if you don't have the ability to test the product first, you may go straight to licensing at this point.

If you have the money, you're well advised to do some test marketing. That's the good thing. If you don't have the option, then you'll go straight to licensing. However, testing will almost always provide information that will improve your odds. In the case of my first commercial invention, I don't think I could have licensed it without having proved it in the marketplace first. That made all the difference. In addition, testing greatly accelerated the licensing negotiations. We were able to move through the process very quickly. And once I had that success, it was easy to duplicate with other inventions.

With experience, you can make sound decisions on your second and third and tenth inventions that you can't make without incurring sizable risks today. When you're first starting, it's so valuable if you have the opportunity to test the product without mortgaging the house. I'm not telling you to take a huge risk on this. That's not my suggestion, but I would recommend it if you can afford it.

The tenacity and the perseverance that this business demands aren't any different than are required in starting any other successful enterprise. And if you talk to anyone who has really made it, they'll tell you it didn't come easily, that they had to work very hard to get where they are, and if you're willing to do that, I think you, too, can succeed. Certainly, the tools and resources available to us as independent inventors are better than ever.

Here's a true story that you might think about for a few minutes, when you aren't feeling rushed or pressured. When Thomas Alva Edison created his first invention, *he didn't know nearly as much as you do this very minute about making the journey from dream to reality.* In light of what he ultimately achieved, I find that thought to be encouraging.

* * *

Phase 6c

Producing Your Invention Yourself

by Jack Lander
Inventor, author, entrepreneur

You will recall that in the Introduction to this book I presented the success statistics gathered by Ron Westrum and Ed Zimmer. First-time inventors who produced their own inventions succeeded about 49 percent of the time, as against the 13 percent success rate for inventors who chose to license. Tempting, right? But producing your invention means ongoing hard work. Most of us have to work full time to provide income for our living expenses (and our inventions), and the additional effort required to launch a product may represent an unmanageable burden.

I should add that in the previous section (6b), Lisa Lloyd gave you a "graduate course" on how to license your invention. Following Lisa's advise, your odds will almost certainly be greater than 13 percent.

However, many of us hope that income from our inventions will eventually enable us to become self employed. This section will help you decide whether you should produce or license your invention, and provide some basic guidance if you decide to produce it.

Producing your invention does not mean that you have to set up a small production facility in your garage or basement. There are ways to delegate nearly all of the tasks demanded by producing. You can orchestrate and delegate these tasks, and reduce your workload to a comfortable level. But each task that is delegated usually takes a toll on your revenue, and likely will reduce your net profit. But not always. If your sales volume increases because you have engaged an effective marketing organization, you may very well earn more profit in an absolute sense, if not a relative sense.

Whether you orchestrate and delegate, or do most of the work yourself, you must consider whether you have the *personal qualities* to manage your own business. Highly creative inventors usually find routine work, such as talking to customers, assembling parts, filling orders, preparing invoices, keeping books, paying bills, and nagging their customers to pay money that is owed, to be boring - - an interruption to their creative work. They want the freedom from corporate regimentation, but they don't want to pay the price of the essential self-imposed discipline.

The entrepreneurial personality, on the other hand, recognizes the opportunities provided by innovation, but considers innovative products mainly as a way to enter business, and earn an exceptionally good living. To the "pure" entrepreneur, innovation is a means, not an end. The element of uncertainty in producing and marketing an unproven product adds challenge and excitement to his or her venture. Winning the game is the motive. Recording more dollars flowing in than flowing out is the way to keep score.

Most of us have personalities that lie somewhere between the extremes of the genius inventor and the hard-driving entrepreneur. And most of us must compromise how we devote time to the creative and the routine aspects of our work, whether for the corporation or for ourselves. In any event, give considerable thought to whether you are willing and able to make the compromises essential to producing your invention. Ask the opinion of close friends and relatives as to which way you lean. Try to not disclose the answer you want. Phrase your questions objectively.

Sourcing.

The five main aspects of producing are these:

- Vendor communication;
- components purchasing;
- assembly purchasing;

- packaging services; and
- warehousing and fulfillment.

The vehicle of **vendor communication** at the component and assembly stages is the drawing. This is often called the "engineering drawing." This drawing is best done on computer using a CAD program. Engineering drawings for components must have exact dimensions for each feature, usually length, width, and thickness (or height, width, and depth, etc.) The tolerances of each dimension must also be noted. The word "tolerance" here is a precise and traditional term used by drafters, engineers, and vendors. A tolerance on a dimension creates an *economic agreement* between the customer and the vendor that works to the advantage of both. The customer gets precision that is sufficient for his or her application; and the vendor gets relief from having to take heroic and time-consuming measures to hold precision that is not important to the end result.

For example, if your invention's length is 10 inches, and this is a somewhat arbitrary dimension, a tolerance of plus or minus 1/16th inch is certainly acceptable to you, and easy (thus, less expensive) for the vendor. Such dimension will appear on the drawing as 10.00 +/- .06. But if you have two parts that must fit together in an assembly, a tolerance of plus or minus .005 (five thousands of an inch) may be appropriate.

Economic tolerancing is the single most troublesome aspect of making drawings. Too loose, you save money, but your parts might not fit together or function properly. Too tight, and your parts fit together like a Swiss watch - - and cost accordingly. Discuss this issue with your designer or drafter, and be sure that you have a good feeling about the person's experience level in selecting tolerances. Also, consult with your component vendors about the tolerances on your drawings, and ask if they are practical from his or her standpoint.

To find CAD drafters, look in your state's *BUSINESS TO BUSINESS* yellow pages, or regular yellow page directory under "Draftsmen" (sorry, ladies, but the yellow page categories tend to be years behind the times.) The *BUSINESS TO BUSINESS* directory is available at your library or from your phone company.

If your design is not well-conceived, you may need a designer rather than a drafter. The difference is that designers know something about materials, methods, tolerances, etc., and drafters usually do not make decisions on these matters.

Find designers in the same directory under "Designers, Industrial." Some designers hold engineering degrees, and some have learned their art as apprentices to senior designers or engineers. Their education is less important than their experience with your kind of components.

Component vendors are called "job shops." Job shops do not make any of their own products, but produce work to their customer's specifications, which are communicated using an engineering drawing, as covered above.

Job shops specialize in one kind or one class of manufacturing. For example, most plastic parts are made by the injection molding process. Most parts cut from plastic sheet stock in small quantities are cut by laser or abrasive water jet, both of which are often found at the same vendor, and are used in cutting metal parts as well as plastic.

If you use an industrial designer, as suggested above, his or her service should include explaining the kind of job shop that is appropriate for each component *at the quantity level you will be purchasing.* If you are planning to make a first production run of perhaps 200 parts, and one of your components is made from sheet metal, this part can be stamped from a die set (possibly $15,000 for the die, and 25 cents each for parts), or it can be abrasive water jet or laser cut using a computer program (around $50 to $100 for the program, and

$1.00 each for parts).

I wish that I could have this paragraph printed in red type for emphasis: you absolutely **must** become well informed about process options. I can't tell you how many times an inventor tells me he has spent several thousand dollars for tooling because he didn't know about a low-tooling-cost process for making his part. Do not - - repeat, do not - - depend on vendors to guide you to the most economic process. For one thing, many, if not most, vendors are myopic about their own process. They simply don't follow the other processes, and *the medium to high volume vendors don't know* what is going on in low-volume manufacturing. Also, it is expecting too much to have a job shop injection molder tell you something like: "You could save a lot of money if you made your part in a silicone rubber mold until you were sure of the market and your volume needs. Then, come back to me, and I'll make you a mold that suits your higher volume needs."

Until you are confident concerning the quantity you will be able to sell on a sustained basis, you should consider spending more for the parts, and saving big dollars on tooling. *Nearly every production process has one or more short run processes that produce equivalent parts.* The only certain way to determine the least expensive method of manufacturing your components is to *solicit price quotations from three or more vendors for each optional process, and to do this for a range of purchase quantities.*

Some vendors are loaded with work, and will quote a high price merely because they don't need the work unless they can make an extra high profit on your job. Others are eager to get business, and will quote lower. Some shops have more modern equipment than others, and can produce at less expense than their competitors. Others have older equipment that is paid for, and even though less efficient, produces parts at significantly less cost than the "latest and greatest" robotic monster. Repeat: The only certain way to determine your lowest purchase cost is to:

1) forecast a range of quantities you believe practical.
2) determine the optional processes for manufacturing.
3) solicit prices from several vendors for each process.
4) insist that each price quote isolate the *nonrecurring* items, mainly tooling and computer programs, so that if you order again these costs are not lumped in with your unit costs, and you pay an unfair price.

You can find out more about appropriate production processes by going to www.jobshop.com on the Internet. A valuable book (price: around $100) is McGraw-Hill's handbook, *Design for Manufacturability,* by Bralla.

Assembly vendors are found in the yellow pages under Assembly and Fabricating Service, etc. Your State's *Business to Business* directory is usually better than your local yellow page directly because it includes ads from vendors in outlying areas that are convenient, but not included in local directories.

The principles of component purchasing apply also to assembly services. Every custom purchase involves a certain amount of one-time (nonrecurring) cost for the vendor. If this is lumped in with the unit price, you end up paying for it over and over. Assembly may involve fixtures and special tools. Insist that any such items be quoted as separate from the unit price.

As your assembly quantity increases, you should expect the price per unit to decrease due to "learning" (efficiency gained with experience), and because the job setup time is spread over more pieces. (See "Principle #7: Solicit prototype pricing professionally" in my chapter on prototyping for details.) Because assembly is nearly always a manual task when we purchase relatively small quantities, assembly time per unit often drops dramatically - - much more than in the production of machined parts.

Packaging.

Packaging contractors are not hard to find, especially if you live in a moderately industrial area. Look in your *Business to Business* yellow pages or the *Thomas Register* under "Packaging Service." Both are found at your library.

Again, the purchasing principles are the same: There will be a tooling or setup charge that will either be quoted as a separate item, or lumped in with the per-package cost. Insist that this charge be isolated, and refuse to do business with vendors who won't. Note: some vendors confuse the terms tooling and setup. Tooling is something you should pay for *only once.* Setup you will pay for *each time* you order. Again, be tough on vendors who don't use these terms correctly. Make them tell you what the elements of "setup" are. (See "Principle #7: Solicit prototype pricing professionally," in the chapter on prototyping for details.)

Packaging services may take your package and your product, and put them together. Or, they may be a full service vendor that creates and produces the package as well as does the actual work of placing your product in the package. Design vendors are found under the heading "Designers, Packaging" in my *Business to Business* yellow pages.

There are basically two kinds of packages: display and non-display. For consumer items, display packaging is extremely important to "selling the seller" as well as selling to the ultimate consumer. A nonprofessionally designed package may prejudice a distributor or retailer. Non-display packages are often used for items that are ordered through catalogs. Catalog houses love nondescript packages on which they can slap a label and postage, and send it on its way when they receive on order for your product alone. Think through the markets you will serve. When you are sure of your markets, consult a professional package designer.

Catalogers, distributors, etc., purchase in "standard box" quantities. A standard box may hold 24, 100, 144, etc. of your unit packages. Standard boxes are more versatile in multiples of 12 because your unit packages can be physically arranged 3 by 4, 2 by 6, or 1 by 12. That's why the dozen is still popular in these days of binary and metric counting.

Warehousing and fulfillment.

Here is one category that the yellow page people are on top of. They have a category captioned "Fulfillment Service." These services warehouse, pack, ship, and even bill your customer. Check several such services to find the one that fits your objectives, as well as to compare costs.

Conclusion and suggestions

- Be sure that you have the personality to start and run your own business. If you find yourself neglecting the routine stuff, maybe you don't have the 'right stuff.'

- Until you are confident of your sales volume, stay with low-cost tooling, and pay a premium for your product. Thomas Edison sold his first light bulbs well under cost in order to establish the market. Market testing may not yield a profit - - except in saving thousands of misspent dollars.

- Don't skimp on package design if your product sells by attracting attention with its package. Use the money you saved on tooling to engage a professional package designer

* * *

Phase 6d

You Only Have One Chance to Make a First Impression

by Joanne Hayes-Rines

Publisher, Inventors' Digest
Vice President, United Inventors Association

Think about what that cliché really means - - especially as it relates to your invention. Are you conscious of the impression you, and your invention, make as you work to develop it into a product?

All too often people are sloppy in the way they present themselves. This "sloppiness" can be the result of ignorance, haste, lack of resources, inexperience, etc. But whatever the reason, in the fast-paced world of the 21st century, first impressions matter more than ever. A negative first impression may end forever your chances to license your invention, interest investors or develop the team you need.

Consider the following scenario

It's Monday morning. An executive of a large company is reviewing her mail. One piece of correspondence arrives in an envelope with a hand-written address and no return address. The envelope holds a three-page letter written on lined, yellow paper with jagged top edges. It contains grammar and spelling errors and is hard to read. The next letter she picks up is typed on good-quality letterhead in perfect style. It is a one-page letter, well written, direct and to the point. Both letters are from inventors who are asking the executive to consider their inventions as possible products to license. If you were the busy executive, which letter would you give more attention to? Which letter would make you think that the inventor had prepared his invention well?

Which letter would entice you to take the next step? Would it be the one that was prepared with care and professionalism or the one that was hastily written? If the inventor doesn't care enough to take the time to make a high-quality, professional presentation, why should the executive take the time with that person?

Remember: *You only have one chance to make a first impression.*

A well thought out, well-executed presentation will not guarantee success, but it most certainly will increase your chances. When you present yourself as a professional, you will be treated as such. Use the following guidelines as you prepare your invention, and yourself, to open that corporate door that may lead you to the licensing agreement that you are looking for.

1. Who are you?

When you introduce yourself to a potential licensee or investor, you are a product developer not an inventor. The word "inventor" often conjures up images of unprofessional, unrealistic dreamers who base their "knowledge" about their product on vague, self-determined "facts." Such people waste other people's valuable time with (usually) worthless ideas.

Product developers know the difference between an idea and an invention. They are developing concepts into viable products that will be accepted in the marketplace and that will make money. Therefore, you are a product developer and NEVER an inventor.

2. Keep it Simple, Stupid (KISS).

Can you define your invention in ten words or less? If not, get busy. Get a piece of paper and write down your definition of what your invention does. Forget what you call it; just write down what it does. For example, "A First Aid Kit that attaches to a stroller" . . . "A Non-Toxic Concrete Cleaner" . . . "A Pie Crust Protector" . . . "Super Lightweight Hiking Gear." Get the idea? Define the invention as succinctly as possible. Why is it important to have a short ten word or less description? Remember that first impression? You want to "grab" your audience with the power and value of your invention; you don't want to bore them to death with a long-winded explanation of why you thought of the idea and why your mother (brother, neighbor, or barber) thinks it's great and why "everyone" will want it.

The KISS theory (Keep It Simple, Stupid) relates perfectly to inventors and inventions. So keep the description to ten words or less.

3. Be realistic.

Included in this book is information about objective invention evaluations from reputable firms and universities. These evaluations are step #1 in preparing information that will support your thesis that your invention is needed, wanted, fulfills a need, can be manufactured at a reasonable cost, etc.

You must be realistic and accurate about your invention's potential. Far too many people present their concepts with exaggerations that are immediately rejected by product reviewers. For example, many people say "everyone" will use their invention. Name a product that everyone uses. The only one I can think of is water (no, not everyone uses toilet paper – babies don't).

Also, obtain realistic manufacturing costs that can be extrapolated into retail prices. The rule of thumb is that manufacturing costs are multiplied by four or five to arrive at retail price. If, for example, it will cost $1 to manufacture your product, then it will sell between $4 to $5. Is this the right price point? Or do you have a product whose competition sells for $2.99? If so, you have to find out how to reduce manufacturing costs before you take the next step. Don't think you can fool a potential licensee or investor; they'll know better than you about the real world costs.

4. Be a professional.
Is your invention a hobby or a business? When you present yourself to an executive, he doesn't want to deal with a hobbyist. He wants to work with a professional so present yourself as one.

The easiest way to create a professional image is to start a business based on your invention. It's not as hard as it sounds. Go to City Hall and find the office where you can register a new business. It may be the City Clerk's office. They will give you an application form that you complete for a new sole proprietor business. One requirement may be to publicize your business application in the local newspaper. Contact the newspaper and ask how to do this. The cost is minimal. After the notice of your application is published in the paper, you will receive a clipping of the notice from the paper. Attach the clipping to the application and submit it with the application fee (fee varies by city – it's approximately $100). Utilize the services of an accountant to understand the financial implications of your business.

Armed with a business name, your next step is to have business cards and stationary printed. Go to a local office supply store where you can get help with design and the information needed on the cards . . . company name, your name, title, address, phone, fax, e-mail, web site. Your cards will read: "Kelly Jones, President." Immediately, you elevate yourself far above those who identify themselves as "an inventor"; you are the president of a company. Now THAT'S a powerful first impression!

5. Know your limits.
Each of us has talents and each of us has liabilities. Be realistic about what you can do yourself and what you need help on. Good at creating letters but terrible at spelling? Don't rely on your computer's spell checker; get a friend or family member to proofread everything you prepare. Terrible at writing? Get help from a professional service or hire a local college student who is studying marketing.

Creating that professional image takes time and energy but it can make the difference between success and futile knocking at doors that never open. Be well prepared when you get the opportunity to make that one-time-only first impression.

* * *

Appendix

Contents:

Other publications of United Inventors Association

- ***THE Inventor's Journal***
  A journal of numbered pages in which you can record your inventions (see Phase 1 in this book).
  ISBN 0-9712367-0-4 $9.95*

- ***THE Inventor's Resource Guide***
  A compact preliminary guide to invention development.
  ISBN 0-9712367-3-9 $9.95*

- ***Starting a Group For Inventors*** by Karyl Lynch
  If you don't have an inventors' networking group in your area, you should start one, as Karyl Lynch did. You don't need to "reinvent the wheel." All of your startup and operating questions are answered in Karyl's book, which she wrote exclusively for UIA.
  ISBN 0-9712367-0-4 $34.95*

*Note: Prices above do not include shipping, which is a flat charge of $3.95 (or current price for 2 pounds via U.S. Post Office Priority Mail) regardless of the number of books or weight. Overseas shipments are at current air mail cost.

Ordering information

Credit card/telephone: 1-716-359-9310
fax: 1-716-359-1132
Checks or money orders: mail to UIA, P.O. Box 23447,
Rochester, New York 14692 USA

Resources

Inventors' Digest magazine. Subscribe through UIA. See ordering information above.

Books and reports on invention developing, patenting, and marketing are available from the UIA's bookstore. Visit our web site at www.UIAUSA.org

U.S. Patent & Trademark Office. General information, prices, patent searching, listing of patent attorneys and agents in your state, etc. are available on its web site: www.uspto.gov

Evaluation of your invention on a confidential basis by the UIA-PIES System, (formerly Wal-Mart Innovation Network). This system was developed by Dr. Gerald G. Udell around three decades ago, and is the most highly respected system in North America. See Phase 2 in this book for more information on evaluation. Obtain your evaluation through UIA. Phone for price: 1-716-359-9310.

Inventor expositions: (not-for-profit organizations only)

Minnesota Inventors Congress, Redwood Falls, Minnesota
Held annually the second weekend in June.
www.invent1.org 1-800-468-3681

Yankee Invention Exposition & Yankee Entrepreneur Workshops
Held annually mid-October in Waterbury, Connecticut
www.yankeeinventionexpo.org 1-203-575-8322 (recording)

Financing Your Invention in The Real World

By Jack Lander
Inventor, author, entrepreneur

Invention financing has five distinct phases: concept investigation; seed money; angel finance; venture capital; and IPO (initial public offering of stock) or private placement.

Except for your credit cards, don't figure on borrowing a significant amount of money on your signature only. Banks are equity lenders; they require either pledged assets (eg., a second mortgage), or a solid history of financial income from your business. Investing in inventions is a high-risk business, and banks are in the low-risk business.

The SBA (Small Business Administration), a branch of the U. S. Department of Commerce, will back a bank loan under certain conditions. Generally, you must already be in business, and you must have orders for your product. Their rules vary from time to time, but don't expect too much.

The *concept investigation* phase starts with the writing of a disclosure that tells in considerable detail the technical features and the benefits of your invention. This paper should be titled Confidential Disclosure to warn all readers that the information contained is not to be shared with others, or made public. Its main use is to clearly explain your invention to the patent searcher and attorney or agent who will write the patentability opinion, and to the university that will provide a commercialization evaluation. See Phase 1 in this book for details.

Based on these two evaluations you must decide whether to proceed or abandon. The typical total cost of these two items will be between $700 and $1,200, which you alone should pay for in order to demonstrate good faith. Convincing others to help you finance your invention is impractical until you have first invested in it yourself. Furthermore, positive evaluations of commercial potential and patent protection provide documentary evidence of your invention's prospects for success.

If your evaluations look promising, and you decide to proceed, your next step is to obtain *seed money,* which is very difficult to get from strangers, such as angel investors. Seed money is used to patent your invention, and make at least one quality prototype. Until you have your patent and your prototype in your hands you simply aren't ready to be taken seriously by professional investors. Seed money is best obtained from close friends and relatives. You will most likely need a total of from $5,000 to $13,000. Figure $4,000 to $10,000 for your patent, and $1,000 to $3,000 for your prototype.

By now, you know that your odds of success are not 100 percent. Inventions are a risky business. And borrowing money from friends and relatives is always a potential source of strained relations. Still, the payback is often excellent when you do succeed. So, rather than borrow, set up a little company and issue stock. Inform your investors that this is a risky venture - - a gamble - - and that if it does not succeed, their investment will be lost.

Get experienced legal advice to set up a small corporation. The term "small" does not just refer to size, but to a special kind of corporation that does not have to follow the same rules for investors as the big guys. But be very cautious about giving up stock; your ability to enlist investors at higher levels is largely determined by the percentage of unissued stock in your treasury.

Repeat: *Get legal advice from an attorney who is experienced in setting up small corporations in your state. Do not attempt this without such counsel.*

Now, with your issued patent and your prototype in hand, you are ready to approach *angel investors* - - well, almost. You will need a polished *business plan* that covers all of the common sense entries, of course. But unless you can argue convincingly that your invention is not a "me too" product, but will earn *extraordinary* profit, your chances of interesting an angel are poor. Also, you must have an *exit strategy* for both you and your angel. Do you want to continue as President? Chief Financial Officer? Do you look forward to "going public," and cashing out yourself and your angel? Angels typically do not want to hang on to a company forever. Their goal is usually to cash out after a certain period of time and/or a certain milestone has been achieved.

Contact your local Small Business Administration office, and ask for assistance in preparing a mature business plan. Also ask for help from SCORE (Service Corps of Retired Executives) and for sources of angel finance. These services are free.

Angel financing is generally used to finance the startup of your company. Angels invest almost exclusively in the fields in which they have expertise. Expect your angel to get intimately involved with your startup, possibly locating people for key positions such as Marketing and Engineering.

Angels cover a wide range of investment dollars, less formalized than venture capital, but typically from about $50,000 to around $2,000,000.

If your startup is successful (not necessarily profitable at this point) and your main problem is how to satisfy sales demand, you are a candidate for *venture capital.* It is said that VC investors look first to the *team*, and then to the product. That doesn't mean that you'll get financing for a great team if your product is uninspiring. Both elements are absolutely essential. So refine your business plan, and submit it to one or more VC groups. VC groups are not interested in ventures that need less than $1,000,000, and more likely $2,000,000. Most proposals are rejected. Rejection doesn't mean that your invention is unworthy; it may just mean that the VC is overbooked, or that your product strays too far from its field of interest - - most often medical or high-tech - - but if you have an exceptional invention, who knows? Offsetting the typical rejection is the abundance of VC groups.

Now, this sequence of financing is sound but not absolutely inviolate. You may be able to work around some of the steps, especially at the angel stage. For example, if you bypass the angel and go directly to the venture capital people, they may be interested enough to recommend the right people who can prepare your company (which may be only you at this point) for the next big leap. Or, your angel may have enough interest and money to sell your company to a larger corporation, or to "take you public" without the need for venture capital.

Wasn't it Confucius who said that the longest journey starts with one step? This exciting journey starts with a simple first step: concept investigation. And you have already taken that step, haven't you?

* * *